BACK TO BALANCE

CRACK YOUR MIND, BODY, SPIRIT CODE TO TRANSFORM YOUR HEALTH

BY: CASSIE SOBELTON

www.CassieSobelton.com

Published by **Archangel Ink**

ISBN: 1942761481
ISBN-13: 978-1-942761-48-8

Table of Contents

Intro

A Note of Gratitude

Life is a journey full of twists and turns that often seem disjointed and unrelated. The farther I walk on my own path, the more I realize there are no accidents and each twist and turn is a major and necessary part of my story. I have tremendous gratitude for the life that has unfolded upon me. The illnesses, the injuries, the jobs and careers, the friends, the foes, the lovers, the doubters, and the naysayers—they have all made a huge impact on who I am and why I am where I am now.

I strongly believe life is an opportunity to learn lessons. I also believe we consciously choose the lessons we are to learn in a specified lifetime and those lessons are presented to us as a series of experiences, challenges, opportunities, achievements, successes, and defeats. Sometimes we are thickheaded and the lesson has to be shown to us over and over again. Other times, we quickly grasp the lesson and move on to the next.

Certain people are brought into our lives to help us learn these lessons. Should those be parents, siblings, lovers, friends, teachers, colleagues, or authority figures, they all have something to teach us. I take serious note when I keep seeing the same type of person enter my life. If that person is someone who brings unwanted feelings, I am clearly overlooking an important lesson. If that person is bringing desirable feelings and experiences, I am on track and see this as a compass telling me so.

Every now and again in life, there are major influencers. For me, those were a series of illnesses and injuries, coupled with an angel that arrived in my teen years to help me navigate them. The angel who came into my life was my stepfather, Chuck O'Brien. My life, this book, and all the wonderful things that have happened to me would have never happened without his interception. He taught me discipline, integrity, kindness, spirituality, moderation, leadership skills, compassion, how to define and hold personal boundaries, and possibly the most important, self-love.

Chuck was truly an angel, and I have missed him every single day since he departed this earth, but the lessons he taught me and the changes he made in me live on. I am extremely grateful for the divine intervention of his presence in my life.

I must also acknowledge my entire family and their contribution to my growth and success. They have all been sources of extreme inspiration. Like all families, we've had our ups and downs. But with the help of positive outlooks, respectful boundaries, and open channels of communication, we have come out stronger for our differences, with love and respect that is unbreakable.

Lastly, there are many friends and teachers who have made an enormous impact on my personal growth and development. There are too many to name, but the one who stands out as it relates to this book is Preya Shah. Although I have been blessed with a bountiful network of supportive, encouraging, loving friends and teachers, I would have never been able to accomplish what I have without her support, love, and encouragement through this process.

I am truly blessed and grateful.

Chapter 1

My Story

Have you ever had the suspicion that your physical challenges are trying to teach you something? What if chronic conditions or recurring injuries are actually a higher power's way of communicating with you, but you just don't have the tools to decipher the message? What if your body is a compass for messages from a spirit (God, a higher power, the Universe, whatever you call it) that points you in the direction you are meant to go?

I truly believe we are all here for a purpose. I believe Earth is like a school, and just like every school year, the classes and tests seem difficult to us at the time, but the answers are always there. When you were in first, second, third grade, and so on, you didn't know the answers to the tests until you studied them, took the test, and received back the graded paper. However, the answer key was there all along, and the answers were already known by so many who had gone before you.

I think this is a wonderful analogy for life. Every answer is already here. Every. Single. One. And our job as humans is to find the answer in the easiest, most efficient and effective way possible. I have found the answers come a billion times easier when I am in balance. When my mind, my body, and my spirit are aligned, life is effortless. The right doors open. The right people show up. The right situations fall in my lap. I like to call this place "the holy flow." When I'm in the holy flow, everything happens for a reason. It's like I'm on a river that is flowing in the perfect direction at all times, without a care in the world, and everything I could ever dream of shows up on my path. Things just keep getting better and better. It seems surreal at times.

Then, there are the times I fall out of balance. You know the times. Life is a struggle. Your body manifests physical problems. Your relationships are all strained. Your job feels more difficult than ever. You have a million worries. There never seem to be enough hours in the day. It's clear you can't keep up like this for long, and inside, you are dying for help. Maybe you turn to your physician (and possibly pharmaceuticals). Maybe you turn to an addiction (food, alcohol, drugs, exercise, toxic relationships, etc.). Others shut down emotionally because it's just too much.

There are many paths we can take when we get to this place, which many of us inevitably will at some point in life. Like most, I was raised in something less than an ideal situation. My life began in a state of imbalance. Being raised by multiple people, seeing many marriages and divorces, my childhood life was far from secure. This manifested in my life as me becoming a very unbalanced young woman, relying on addictions as the only source of food for my soul.

After a lifetime of wake-up calls (injuries, a decade of illness, and major surgery after major surgery), I had an epiphany. I woke up to the mind-body-spirit connection and changed my life. I found balance, and it brought about healing on every level. A reformed party girl (or "numbing-out expert") turned mind-body-spirit expert, my life goal is to help others achieve their version of mind-body-spirit balance in simple and easy steps, leading to upgraded health and endless possibilities.

In the pages that follow, I have condensed decades of research and personal study on the mind, the body, and the spirit. It is my belief that, just like the legs of a tripod, all three need to be equally addressed, tended to, and maintained in order to achieve and maintain balance. It took many years for me to integrate these suggestions into my life, and this is not intended to be a manual of changes you need to make immediately. This is meant to be a gentle guide and explanation of some of the things you can do, slowly over time, to improve each area of your life.

Remember the three E's: easy, efficient, and effective. The last thing I want you to do is stress out over anything, especially this book. That completely defeats the purpose of finding balance. If the suggestions are something you think you can add into your life with ease, then I want you to do it. If not, I want you to put it in the back of your mind for a later date.

A huge part of life is having seeds planted that will eventually grow. Maybe some of these suggestions will be incorporated later in your life, and that is perfectly all right. I want you to focus on the ones you can currently implement with ease. I encourage you to pick one or two upgrades per chapter to implement. Maybe you'll save this book, read it again in a year, and pick another few. You have your entire life to implement new strategies, change behaviors, and incorporate new ideas. Don't rush it. Go slow. Remember that balance is a moving target, and, most important, HAVE FUN!

If you are currently suffering from an illness, injury, or ailment that has taken you from doctor to doctor and no one can seem to help you, you could easily be at the end of your rope. If you suffer from a chronic condition that has successfully taken over your life, you are likely sick and tired of being sick and tired.

I know this story because it is my own. By the time I was in my mid-20s, I had been through more surgeries than most people go through in their entire lives. I had three major knee surgeries; left tibia replacement with a cadaver bone; a ruptured appendix; and surgery to remove a tumor in my large intestines, along with the majority of my colon and many feet of my small intestines. I was also diagnosed with severe Crohn's disease, which went undiagnosed for a decade and wreaked absolute havoc on my life, amongst other small surgeries and issues.

I've been there. I know a thing or two about pain, frustration, and the confusion it causes. And I am finally at a place now where I can see it all as it is—a gift. The gift of growth, the gift of opportunity, the gift of victory, and the biggest, most unexpected gift of all: *the ability to use my body as a compass for that which spirit is trying to teach me.*

I admit it took me a long time to accept this idea. I thought I was cursed or just had horrible luck. I couldn't understand why all these horrible things kept happening to me. I hadn't yet figured out that I was in a place vibrationally, or spiritually, that attracted out-of-balance experiences into my life. My body was being used as a tool for the higher realms to communicate with me.

It wasn't until I studied the work of Louise Hay that I started to open my mind to the possibility that my body was trying to show me what my mind, or ego, was denying. Years earlier, I had read one of Louise's books, *Heal Your Body A-Z: The Mental Causes for Physical Illness and the Way to Overcome Them*, and thought it was nonsense. But the seed had been planted, and when synchronicity made me stumble upon that book again, I gave it another read. This book detailed the possible mental causes of illnesses and injuries and, oddly enough, when I read the physical ailments that some of my family or friends had, the mental causes were spot on! It was like Louise knew them personally.

This forced me to read again the mental causes for intestinal issues, which were "fear of letting go, and holding on to the past." They sounded nothing like me, but I knew I was on to something. If the mental causes were so accurate for everyone around me, they had to be true for me too, right? I thought that I must be in denial; my ego was not allowing me to see my faults. The more I thought about this, the more I took it to heart. The more I took it to heart, the more I started to realize I had to make some changes if I wanted to live a healthy, happy life. And I was ready. I had been broken down into a million pieces too many times. I was so beat up; it seemed to be the only option. It was time to do the work. It was time to get to the bottom of my emotional problems, own them, and release them so I could start a new life full of joy, endless possibilities, love, and happiness.

It is much easier to stay in balance than it is to come back into balance. This is why preventative medicine is making such huge waves in today's medical system. This is true for the body, the mind, and the spirit. Since they are all so interconnected, it's difficult to accurately look at them individually, but somehow we managed to separate them in Western medicine. Preventative and holistic approaches to health have been the staple of Eastern medicine for centuries and have served their population very well. Unfortunately, many of the traditions and much of the knowledge have been lost or discarded by modern medicine.

After my major Crohn's surgery, I was sent home with more pills to take than imaginable. I lived an extremely unhealthy lifestyle at the time, and I remember asking my physician, "What about my diet?" He shrugged it off and told me I'd be on these medications for the rest of my life. Something inside of me knew it wasn't true. I didn't think he was deliberately lying to me or trying to hurt me, but most Western physicians are not trained in nutrition, lifestyle modifications, or the mind-body-spirit connection. They are trained in pharmaceuticals. And true to their training, it's what they practice. Fair enough. But I didn't want to live that way. I didn't want to live the rest of my life consulting my pillbox seven times a day. I didn't want to go back in for the next surgery they said I needed, which was to have a colostomy bag put in. I didn't want to be sick the rest of my life. I didn't want to be "the girl that has Crohn's disease." I wanted to enjoy life. I wanted to enjoy the foods at parties and restaurants and family meals. I wanted to live. I wanted to heal. And I was determined to find out how.

I started researching everything I could find about holistically healing the body. I talked to every holistic practitioner that would take my call. I enrolled in every class I could find that claimed to teach natural healing. I spent every dollar I made on my education of these subjects. After one year, I was off all my medications, had lost 40 pounds, and felt better than I could ever remember feeling. I cracked the code—MY CODE.

We all have different codes, and no two people will experience the same results from any one practice. The key is to explore, to become educated, to experiment on yourself and use your intuition as an emotional guidance system that helps you figure out what works for YOU and what doesn't. This is how you can heal yourself. This is how you WILL heal yourself. I absolutely promise you: it IS possible.

Understanding that most of us can't (or won't) give up a decade of life to research and study this information, I strongly encourage you to use your intuition while reading this book to figure out what it is that YOU need to implement in YOUR life. If you feel drawn towards something, I highly recommend you implement it and watch what it does for you. I also suggest keeping a journal where you log what you are doing and how it affects you or different things you want to try. Remember to keep an open mind, because it just might be possible that not all things are as they seem. Ideas and practices that make no sense whatsoever at first often have merit.

What's the worst that could happen if you try a crazy new idea? You might waste a few dollars or moments of your time. Big deal. What if it works? What if the incorporation of many things in this book actually restores your balance? What if the search for health and happiness is over and the trips from doctor to doctor are too? What if you find a way to heal your body, your mind, and your spirit? What if it really is this simple, but we live in a society that has downplayed it and led us to believe it's not possible? What if you really are ready and this is the first day of your new life? Be open-minded, my friend. I assure you it's a lot easier than having it blown open one day.

Chapter 2

Mind-Body-Spirit Tripod

I encourage you to consider the mind, the body, and the spirit as a tripod. Focusing on all three will lead to the most powerful transformation and the opportunity to reverse disease on all levels. Like a table with three legs, your health is only as strong as each leg. Looking at the entire person (the mind, the body, and the spirit) is an approach that most Western medical practitioners are not trained in. Rather than seeing the entire picture, the body is the only piece that is treated. All three areas need to be treated for healing to occur.

When most of us who live in Western civilizations think "holistic healing," we think of a "witch doctor" or "hippie medicine." We have somehow confused these terms with holistic medicine, which means to treat the whole person while taking into account mental, social, spiritual, and physical symptoms of a disease. When I talk about a holistic approach to wellness, I'm asking you to look at your body, your health, and your life as one whole entity instead of thinking of them as separate. It's about skipping the quick fix of a Band-Aid treatment and treating the root cause of a problem, which incorporates the mind and spirit into the treatment. This takes a bit longer than we are accustomed to in Western medicine, so patience and determination must also be practiced. However, the reason it takes more time is because we are fixing the cause, not just temporarily taking care of the symptoms. This will lead to true healing and a long-term solution.

Thinking of your own personal tripod, how do your individual legs look in comparison to the others? Are your mind, your body, and your spirit all strong and supportive of each other? Is any one of them more dominant than the others? If you were a tripod, would you be standing tall and stable or leaning over, close to toppling?

What kind of habits do you have in your life supporting each leg? Understanding that each leg of the tripod supports the others and healthy habits support all three is key to keeping yourself in balance. Proper nutrition in the form of quality, whole foods, plays a role in feeding the body what it needs to thrive and assisting the body to remove toxins and chemicals that are harmful. Proper nutrition is also necessary for the gut to make the hormones and neurotransmitters necessary for the mind to experience happiness. Proper nutrition also allows you to connect spiritually by activating the production of hormones in the pineal gland, which is also called the "third eye" and is strongly associated in many spiritual texts to a higher power.

Movement is an important part of the mind, body, and spirit integration. Movement strengthens all three legs, just like nutrition. Movement's benefits to the body are widely known and accepted, but it also supports the mind by producing chemicals and hormones that support a positive mood and outlook. It even supports your connection to spirit by helping you release emotions that are stored in your body and which are blocking a connection to a higher power. Many people experience emotional shifts or breakthroughs when practicing yoga because they get into positions that help release certain areas of the body that tend to store emotion.

We will explore many other ways that you can integrate and strengthen the mind, body, spirit connection as the book goes on. It is important to remember that it didn't take you one day to get where you are. You have lived a lifetime that has slowly taught you habits that now make up your routine. You started learning lifestyle habits from those who raised you. This moved on to your first living experience outside of the family, be it with friends, a lover, college dorms, or alone. Each living situation or living partner brought more habits that slowly became part of your lifestyle. Outside influences have a way of creeping in and slowly becoming part of you. This is why it is said that you should be careful whom you spend your time with, as you are most like the five people to whom you are closest.

If that is truly the case, if you are most like the five people you spend the most time with, you might want to take a hard look at their lives and ask yourself, "*Are they living the way I want to live?*" Maybe you can find a new friend or two who are living the way you strive to live and spend more time with them. Whether you realize it or not, you are influenced by the people around you each day. You're influencing the people you are around, as well. When you are ready to make change, it's always easier to have people in your inner circle who are already living the change you want to make.

If, over the years, you slowly made a lifestyle out of the habits you were exposed to without even realizing it, it makes sense that you can slowly start incorporating healthier habits and reverse your lifestyle habits towards a healthier life, yes? Unless you have an illness that is of grave concern, a slow, realistic approach to change is most likely to succeed.

Often the first step you should take towards a more holistic lifestyle is cleaning up your diet. As a culture, we are becoming more and more aware of the harmful and often toxic ingredients in our food. Things have changed dramatically over the last few decades, and the rates of disease have skyrocketed. It's obvious the correlation is strong, but sometimes the problem seems so big and insurmountable that you may not know where or how to begin. If you talk with many of the "experts" in the holistic nutrition world, they will scare the daylights out of you. They'll make you think you can't eat anything ever again. Their approach is so rigid and over-the-top, the average person thinks it's impossible and just decides not to try. And I don't blame them. Not one bit!

Food is where I intuitively began, and looking back, it made a lot of sense since I was on a mission to heal a digestive disorder. I started with absolutely no formal training on the subject but followed my intuition on both what to eat and where to study. I thought I was doing something great for my body and I was. But, I didn't realize I was also doing something wonderful for my mind and my spirit by cleaning up my diet. I was mentally clear, focused, determined, and happier. Eating properly gave me a whole new outlook on life and eating raw foods started to give me a feeling of connection to higher realms. At the time, I wasn't sure what was happening, but now that I've studied foods' effects on the mind and spirit, it is obvious.

Then, when I started feeling so connected spiritually, I became a better overall person. I became more loving, giving, and compassionate. I started extending help to others and offering assistance that created good will, not only in my life, but in the lives of others. It was a ripple effect. And once you start, you'll be shocked at what shifts in your life and how your mind, body, and spirit will all benefit. Your taste buds will change. You'll stop craving the old, bad foods and start craving the new, healthy foods you are exposing yourself to. You'll start stocking fresh fruits and vegetables and grabbing those instead of processed food. You'll start playing around with new recipes and learn about healing spices. Spices that assist in healing will start to appeal to you and you'll find yourself craving things your body needs because your mind and spirit are so in tune with what you need.

Once you make a habit of moving your body, you will actually CRAVE movement. Your body will feel great because it's getting the movement necessary to feel good. Your mind will start to make the happy hormones and neurotransmitters necessary to keep your mood positive and upbeat. You will start to feel happier and healthier. You will start to move stuck energy in your body and boost your brain chemistry, which will integrate the mind-body-spirit connection.

Have you ever been so angry you wanted to punch something? Or so excited you wanted to jump up and down and scream? Or so happy to see someone that you wanted to run towards them and tackle them with your love? When you have emotions or stored energy in the body, it is your innate desire to express that emotion. Most people feel this when it's a big feeling, but very few are in tune enough to feel this way with all the small emotions that build up during the day. And when you don't feel it, you don't express it. And expressing it is what releases it.

Some of you may have a lifestyle or jobs that allow you to express emotions that would otherwise be stored in the body without you even knowing. Those who have regular movement in your jobs should be thankful, as that movement helps release those emotions that could otherwise be storing up on a daily basis. But those of you sitting at a desk or in a stationary position for many hours a day still have those emotions creeping up, without the movement to help release them. This is where you need to pay attention. This is where you need to focus on daily movement so those emotions don't store up and cause dis-ease.

It wasn't until I became interested in yoga and meditation that I started to understand the correlation between movement and stored emotion. Or maybe I became interested in yoga because I was starting to understand the mind-body-spirit correlation. Who knows? It's interesting the way the right people started to show up on my path at the right time to integrate all this in my mind. This is why I urge you to just go try something. Go try a fitness class. Go try a yoga class. Go learn meditation. Go meditate with various groups of people. Go meet people who are living the way you would like to live and watch how quickly the teachers appear and the teachings unfold.

It was all these fabulous people showing up in my life at the right time with the right information that took me to the next level of understanding. I started to put the pieces together about the mind-body-spirit correlation and how the lack of understanding was causing me unnecessary suffering. Prior to this, I hadn't put together the cause and effect of my actions and how they turned into dis-ease in my body.

Our society hasn't done us any favors by downplaying this ancient knowledge. We have been taught to numb out, tune out, and check out. We have been desensitized, demoralized, and commercialized. If we don't feel right, we have been conditioned to purchase something to make ourselves feel better. Just watch any television show and the commercials within. Food, medications, or whatever the new shiny object of the month is will be plastered in your mind, the commercials touting it as the next feel-good purchase. You may know what is going on consciously. You know these things won't bring true, long-term happiness. But you are acting the majority of the time from a subconscious level. Researchers estimate that the subconscious mind rules decision-making 95% of the time. This means only 5% of your decisions come from a place of consciousness.

Dr. Bruce Lipton is a brilliant author and scientist I have followed closely through the years. I have also had the pleasure of meeting him, spending time listening to his teachings, and learning how the subconscious mind's programs are set by the time we are six years old and automatically react to situations with stored-behavior responses. There are ways we can break these patterns, though. First and foremost is learning how to consciously deal with and release your emotions so they're not driving unwanted behavior.

I have found the most efficient and effective way to do this is with meditation and proper body movement. In the chapters that follow, we will dive deeper into the mind-body-spirit connection and how you can start to integrate practices into your life that will absolutely change your relationship with yourself. You will gain a well-rounded understanding of how your emotions, the energy in your body, and your mind/ body/ spirit work together to create balance and harmony or, to the contrary, a state of dis-ease. You will learn how to navigate this terrain for yourself, as no one else can do it for you. You will be empowered to take ownership of your health, your life, and your happiness. I'm so grateful to be guiding you on this journey and am so proud of you for taking the first step, which is to gain understanding and knowledge that will forever change your life!

Chapter 2 Checklist

1. Start to look for the connection between your mind, body, and spirit.

- Notice how you feel physically, mentally, emotionally, and spirituality after making poor food choices versus engaging in proper nutrition.
- Notice how your body reacts to stressful situations. (For example, are headaches or stomachaches a common theme after stressful events?)
- When you correlate physical symptoms to emotional situations, are there other ways you could alleviate the symptoms if you are currently using medications?

2. Keep your eyes open for synchronistic signs and opportunities to upgrade your health.

- Look for flyers for fitness, yoga, or meditation classes in your life.
- Accept invitations to attend a class or take a walk with a friend or colleague.
- Watch for group sports or different activity clubs to present themselves.

3. Incorporate movement into your job so you are moving more often during the day.

- Switch to the printer that is down the hall instead of the one at your desk.
- Commit to always use the bathroom on another floor, taking the stairs to get there.
- Move your files and office supplies across the room so you have to get up to access them.
- Look for other ideas specific to your office space: repetitive movements are an opportunity–anything you do often can be moved further away to encourage movement.

4. Seek out people living the life you want to live. Make it a point to spend more time with these types of people, keeping in mind that you are a reflection of the five people you spend the most time with.

5. Start to look at your health more holistically, looking for ways one leg of your tripod might be balancing or unbalancing the others.

Chapter 3

Imbalance Manifests in the Body as Dis-ease

Many of you may wander through life without putting together the pieces of the puzzle or connecting the dots between your physical ailments and your mental situations. What if, just like children who do not see the correlation between the puppets moving and the strings held by the puppeteers, you do not yet see the cause and effect of the mental situations that cause physical manifestations?

That's where I was when I got sick. I was in total denial of the possibility that my thoughts could be causing my illness and thought that theory was absolute nonsense. But, in reality, my body was literally DYING for me to see the truth. My ego was so large (and in charge) that I couldn't see how screwed up my mind was or begin to correct it. Now I am in a much different place.

After nearly two decades of "doing the work," diving deep into my emotional stuff and facing things head-on, I can tell you that every single person on this earth is manifesting physical conditions in their body based upon what is happening in their mind and spirit. Now when I talk to people and they tell me what is going on with them physically, I know what is going on with them mentally. I get glimpses of their personality based on these ailments. Of course, this is wonderful knowledge to have as a human, but more important, it helps me direct them to healing those emotional wounds versus just putting a bandage on the ailment itself.

I feel strongly that physical ailments and emotional issues must be tended to at the same time for true healing to occur. That said, I certainly believe the cause is the emotional issue, so if that is corrected, healing can immediately happen, and I believe this is what spontaneous healing is. The majority of us have beliefs and emotions so deep and imprinted from such an early age that spontaneous healing is difficult to achieve. Changing such a deep belief so quickly is tough for our egos, which are powerful in most of us.

With that stated, there are some ways to narrow in on what the mental causes of your ailments are. The chakra system, which you may have seen indicated in drawings as a rainbow of circles that start at the pelvic area and rise to the top of the head, is an ancient system used to depict the meeting points of non-physical energy in the body (otherwise known as the subtle body). There are channels in your subtle body through which vital energy (also called prana or life force) flows. The concept of chakras is present in Hinduism, Buddhism, and yogic traditions, but many religions reference the same idea without the word "chakra." For example, think about the pictures of Christ with a glowing halo, which happens to surround the head (which is the 7th chakra, the chakra that indicates a cosmic understanding or connection to a higher power).

Each of the seven chakras correlates with specific thought processes, mental conditions, organs, and other body parts; even different foods and herbs are said to block or open these energy centers. When we talk about the seven chakras, we start with the 1st chakra at the base of the spine and move up through the body to the top of the head, which is the 7th.

1st Chakra—Root or Base Chakra

Color—Red

Location—Base of the spine

Purpose—Foundation of the physical body; assists in keeping us grounded to the earth

Influences—Immune system, energy, basic impulses, instincts, endurance, fight-or-flight reactions

Deals with—Survival (including food, protection, shelter)

Balanced—If relationships in early life were good quality, supportive, loving

Unbalanced—If relationships in early life were stressful, poor quality, unsupportive, unloving

Relevant to—Achievements in the material world, stability, strength of character, patience, safety

When Balanced—Feelings of health, happiness, optimism, vitality

When Too Little Energy Flowing—Could cause lack of follow-through and confidence, excess anxiety, feelings of being unloved, masochism

When Too Much Energy Flowing—Could cause overpowering of others, aggression, sadism, greediness, or selfishness

Where it Manifests in the Body—Legs, bones, adrenal glands, colon, kidneys, and spine

Can Balance Chakra by—Dancing, jumping, squatting, showering, or submerging yourself in water

2nd Chakra—Sacral or Sexual Chakra

Color—Orange

Location—Lower abdomen (approximately two inches below belly button)

Purpose—Source of purpose and creativity, foundation of the emotional body

Influences—Sexuality, physical force, love, open-mindedness, ability to cooperate with others

Deals with—Ability to feel and let go of emotions and sensations

Balanced—If creative, open-minded, cooperative

Unbalanced—If emotional or sexual problems; excess food, sex, or drugs

Relevant to—Intuition, energy, success, good frame of mind, learning from experiences, focus needed to attain goals

When Balanced—Feeling of health, openness, kindness, creativity, friendliness, tolerance, patience

When Too Little Energy Flowing—Shyness, hyper-sensitivity, confusion, uncertainty, aimlessness, lack of trust

When Too Much Energy Flowing—Self-centered, too ambitious, jealous, cold, lack of trust

Where it Manifests in the Body—Lower abdomen, spleen, liver, bladder (bladder infections), kidneys, sexual organs, fertility and reproduction, impotence, frigidity

Can Balance Chakra by—Dancing, laughing, enjoying friend's company

3rd Chakra—Solar Plexus Chakra

Color—Yellow

Location—Base of rib cage

Purpose—Foundation of mental body

Influences—Muscles, stomach, digestion, pancreas, liver, gallbladder, metabolism, nervous system

Deals with—Understanding of our own inner workings

Balanced—If we own our power, move forward in life, have self-confidence

Unbalanced—If anger and frustration is dominant, problems dealing with power or authority

Relevant to—Picking up vibrations and energy from everything around us (others, places, and objects), personal power, self-control, self-acceptance, emotional control

When Balanced—Ability to accomplish goals, relax and enjoy, feelings of safety and security, calmness around change and understanding that changes lead to a better life, organized life, concentration improves

When Too Little Energy Flowing—Frustration is represented

When Too Much Energy Flowing—Anger is represented

Where it Manifests in the Body—Digestive problems, ulcers, liver, pancreas

Can Balance Chakra by—walking in nature, spending time in sunlight, sitting in front of the fire or lighting candles

4th Chakra—Heart Chakra

Color—Green

Location—Center of chest (heart area)

Purpose—Love

Influences—Forgiveness, compassion, empathy, trust, ease in life

Deals with—Bringing balance to all parts of ourselves, helping others, becoming humanitarian

Balanced—If the lower three chakras are balanced

Unbalanced—If emotionally unstable, playing the martyr, obsession, feelings of being unloved, suspicion, repression of feelings and memories

Relevant to—Rejuvenation, rebirth, success, growth, prosperity, development

When Balanced—Unconditional love, helping others, feeling of peace within and outside world

When Too Little Energy Flowing—Lack of generosity, holding others down

When Too Much Energy Flowing—Overgiving, playing the martyr, feeling unappreciated

Where it Manifests in the Body—Lungs, heart, thymus, circulation, endocrine system, immune system

Can Balance Chakra by—Spending time in nature, performing random acts of kindness, enjoying a romance novel or movie

5th Chakra—Throat Chakra

Color—Blue

Location—Throat, base of neck

Purpose—Connects our communication with higher realms, using our words to help others grow

Influences—Communication, dreaming, artistic expression, good judgment, wisdom, speaking truth

Deals with—Our ability to communicate our truth

Balanced—If we express freely and honestly without hurting others

Unbalanced—If sore throat, communication issues, earaches or infections, chronic colds, speech difficulties, thyroid problems, tiredness, or depression

Relevant to—Expression, communication

When Balanced—Free communication, happiness, centeredness

When Too Little Energy Flowing—Nervousness, fear, introversion, opposition to change, keeping thoughts to oneself

When Too Much Energy Flowing—Control of others through dishonesty or deceit, inflexible, dominating, egotistical

Where it Manifests in the Body—Mouth, teeth, throat, thyroid, immune system

Can Balance Chakra by—Singing, chanting, meditating

6th Chakra—Third Eye or Brow Chakra

Color—Indigo Blue

Location—Middle of forehead, between eyebrows

Purpose—Insight, enlightenment, awareness

Influences—Capacity to see things coming, defines fantasy and reality

Deals with—Ability to reflect properly on past and sense events before they happen

Balanced—If intuitive, imaginative, able to concentrate and visualize

Unbalanced—If blocked, unable to visualize or imagine, lack of intuition

Relevant to—Enlightenment

When Balanced—Feeling of being in control of life, courage to follow our desires, confidence, sixth sense working well

When Too Little Energy Flowing—Unassertiveness, fear of success, too sensitive to others feelings, unaware of the difference between higher guidance and ego

When Too Much Energy Flowing—Lack of concentration, headaches, confusion, panic attacks, depression

Where it Manifests in the Body—Eyes, vision, nose (sinus issues), nervous system, brain (headaches), pituitary gland

Can Balance Chakra by—Visualizing an indigo blue light during meditation

7th Chakra—Crown Chakra

Color—Violet or white

Location—Top of head

Purpose—Foundation of our spiritual body

Influences—Inspiration, higher understanding, connection to a higher source, spiritual will

Deals with—Our link to the higher realms

Balanced—If easily guided and self-confident in direction

Unbalanced—If apathetic, problems understanding and retaining knowledge

Relevant to—Connection with higher power

When Balanced—Released from ego-driven desires, ability to trust in our higher guidance

When Too Little Energy Flowing—Unsure of our own guidance, reduction of self-confidence, fear, anxiety

When Too Much Energy Flowing—Guided by ego rather than the highest good

Where it Manifests in the Body—Cerebral cortex, nervous system, pineal and pituitary glands and all hormones related to them, headaches, worry, anxiety, immune disorders, cognitive problems

Can Balance Chakra by—Meditation; visualization of a connection to your higher source, inner self, or spirit guides

As you can see, there are many overlaps in the chakra system. Just like one imbalance in the body can lead to many physical issues, one imbalance in the mental or emotional body can lead to many imbalances. You may have noticed the lower three chakras (chakras 1–3) relate to personal energy, while the higher three chakras (chakras 5–7) relate to the self in the collective consciousness of a higher guidance or spirituality. The 4th chakra (the Heart Chakra) is where the physical and spiritual bodies are connected.

Understanding the chakra system is a great tool for self-evaluation. It can really help you look at the mental issues that might be causing a dis-ease to manifest in the body. Have you noticed how I write the word "disease" with a dash between the syllables? This is a great reminder for me every time I use the word that a physical dis-ease is nothing more than a disconnection with ease. It's the opposite of ease. It's what happens to you when you aren't focusing on a mental or spiritual connection. When you are fighting something, you are not at ease. When you are disconnected from your source, you are not at ease. When you are replaying childhood hurts, negative habits, and karmic imprints, you are not at ease.

You ARE at ease when you are living authentically. You are at ease when you are tending to your spiritual and mental growth. You are at ease when you are living from a place of harmony with yourself, others, and the earth. And your body knows it. Your body is so smart and wants you to live the best, most connected life possible.

In our current society, where commercialism and consumerism are driving forces, it's easy to forget what matters in life. It's easy to chase after money, cars, sex, and all things fast. It's easy to forget our connection to a higher power or source. If it weren't for our bodies and their brilliant manifestations that bring us back to center, we could easily waste our entire lives chasing shiny objects that have no meaning.

Luckily, your body is here to stop you from spending your life chasing things that don't matter. Your body is here to show you the way and help you get back on track. Have you ever noticed that people who go through difficult physical times are usually the ones who turn their lives around and find connection? If it weren't for this miraculous process your body takes you through, you could be living in a world that has no "wake-up calls" or "come –to-Jesus moments." Those people who live through these trying times are some of the most inspirational people out there, and many of us never have to experience the same kind of physical pain because we learn through their experiences. What a gift!

Chapter 3 Checklist

1. Take notice of when you are in a mental state of ease or dis-ease throughout your day.
2. Look for opportunities to incorporate more activities that bring a state of ease into your life.
3. Reduce activities that put you into a state of dis-ease throughout your day.
4. Consider the chakra system for self-evaluation.
5. Consider your ailments and which chakra they might be originating from.
6. Contemplate the chakra system and what you might be doing to progress your ailments.
7. Contemplate the chakra system and what you could do to reverse your ailments.
8. Identify when you are chasing "shiny objects" versus meaningful, fulfilling experiences.
9. Consider your pain or dis-ease as a gift of communication from your body.
10. Find opportunities to be grateful for your body's communication.
11. Listen to your body and make adjustments in your life that help bring your body back into ease.

Chapter 4:

Mind—Change Your Mind, Change Your Life

Have you ever considered that the rise in chronic disease is due to an overly disconnected society? As the years go on and we lose our connection to spirit, the increase of dis-ease in our society is staggering. It makes perfect sense.

Think about all the digestive disorders: Crohn's, colitis, IBS, and the like. Think about the chakra system and how many people are suffering from a lack of support and love (or the perception thereof), either now or from their upbringing. I was the poster child for this! And I find most people who come to me suffering with similar issues are in the same situation. The second they acknowledge this and start to correct it, their symptoms disappear.

Don't get me wrong; this is not always a quick or easy process. As a matter of fact, most people deny they have these feelings. I don't think they're "lying," but they might be fooling themselves and are not ready to see the truth. So, this is when I strongly urge people to start meditating or finding ways to connect with spirit. I know that once this process is started, their ego will drop enough for them to see the truth about what is happening in their mind and life. They will start to identify unsupportive and unloving relationships from the past or their current life. Once they see them, they will be ready to change or leave those situations and relationships, should they be with themselves or with others. And this is exactly what I hope and plan for you.

It's not uncommon for people to leave my guidance or counseling when I suggest a spiritual connection is necessary to treat a digestive disorder. I more than understand their hesitation and lack of understanding. So, of course, I also start them on an anti-inflammatory diet and talk to them about stress in their life. But if they aren't ready to look at the tripod of mind-body-spirit, I know the healing will not happen. Sometimes it just takes time for someone to be open to it, and if that's the case, I'll wait it out. But often the person is not ready, so I let them go from my program, knowing I've planted a seed that may one day flower. And often I get a call years later with success stories of spiritual connection and the falling away of symptoms. When you are ready, the path will show itself. It's all about being open and fearlessly looking at your true self. Once you can move past the idea of being embarrassed about your shortcomings and realize your shortcomings are here for you to identify and grow beyond, you will be excited to see your downfalls, as you will know that seeing them is the first step in transmuting them. It's so powerful and exciting!

Admitting your shortcomings is the only way to take your power back and grow. It's so powerful to have the innocence of a child. Think about when a child misbehaves or acts unkindly and how you would bring your child to the side and lovingly explain to him that he hurt someone with his actions and why he should act differently. That child, if young enough, will look at you and say he's sorry and he'll behave better next time. He has no embarrassment of his behaviors. He listens to what you are saying and agrees that he can act better. He then runs over to whomever he's hurt, says "I'm sorry," hugs the person, and just like that, drops the entire incident and moves on with whatever he was doing. THAT is true innocence and an ability we could all embody.

Being able to see your mistakes, admit them, apologize, grow, and move on with life—can you imagine if adults acted like that? Why do we think, once we get beyond a certain age, that we cannot admit our shortcomings or acknowledge our mistakes and make corrections that lead to personal growth? Why must we act so embarrassed and deny our issues to everyone around us, who, by the way, can see our issues clear as day, as well as our denial? Think about that: just like you see everyone else's issues, and most likely see them denying their issues, everyone else sees you and your issues. Do you prefer the people who keep denying and playing out their old habits or do you prefer the people who actively admit their issues, are honest with you and themselves about those issues, and make true apologies and strive to change? I know whom I prefer to be around. And I know whom I prefer to be.

It's not always easy, but like anything, the more you do it, the easier it becomes. Being honest with yourself and starting a practice of personal reflection is one of the most rewarding experiences in human existence. How might you start this practice in your life today? Could you start to meditate so you can clear your unconscious mind and see things as they truly are? Could you ask the five people closest to you for their honest (kind) opinion of what your toughest traits to deal with are? Could you start to journal your thoughts into a book so you could go back and read your words to see if there are any themes to your thought process? Could you start to look at your dis-ease as a vehicle for your subconscious to talk to you and get honest about what might be causing your symptoms? Could you look back on your childhood and start to love and nurture yourself in the ways you were deprived of? Could you take ownership of your life and what has happened to you and how it has affected your mind-body-spirit connection? Could you move from a place of being a victim to a place of seeing everything that happened to you in your life as a gift that you were being given the opportunity to grow beyond? Could you see everything in your life as a blessing and opportunity for growth? Could you see everything that has ever happened to you in your life as something that actually happened FOR you?

Shifting your thinking and learning to see everything as a growth opportunity keeps you constantly moving towards higher realms. If you are ready to make a shift into this kind of living, it will be the most healing and rewarding thing you ever do. Your mind, your body, and your spirit will thank you and delight you with a shift that will change your life in so many ways, you cannot even imagine it. Your ego will be tamed, and you'll stop chasing things that do not matter to you. Your desires will be more in line with the whole of humanity, and your body will rejoice in feeling good because all is in cosmic order and it no longer has to communicate any messages to you.

In addition to getting real with yourself and starting to face what used to be hidden, there are things you can do to assist the mind in feeling good. Food is an intricate piece of this puzzle, as food significantly affects mood. There are neurotransmitters in the body that are needed in order for you to feel good. The most commonly understood example is serotonin. You've probably heard of this hormone (or neurotransmitter) referred to as the "feel-good hormone," and you likely also know that it is bolstered in the body when you exercise. But, what you might not know is that the food you take in on a daily basis contributes to the production of hormones that impact brain health. You need to eat whole foods (vegetables, legumes, fruit, nuts, seeds) to produce the neurotransmitters in the brain necessary for overall brain health.

My dear friend Julie Booksh is a phenomenal alternative therapist who teaches how natural, unprocessed, and fiber-rich foods combined with protein keep the brain sharp, strong, and feeling good. They feed those neurotransmitters that keep us calm, balanced, alert, thinking clearly, motivated, and with the most keen concentration. Food has an even larger role than we once believed, as keeping healthy bacteria in the gut is one of the most important things we can do.

Contrary to popular belief, many neurotransmitters are actually produced in the gut—not the brain—and are then used by the brain to regulate mental processes like learning, memory, and mood. This helps us understand the stronger correlation between what we eat and how it affects our brain chemistry. Superfoods and super herbs, including cacao, turmeric, and many mushrooms, are also extremely effective in helping us produce positive brain chemistry.

So, eating the right foods, eliminating excess sugar, and taking probiotics are not only great for your body, but fabulous ways to increase the health of the brain, leading not only to better functioning, but to better psychological states as well. Again, we see an example of the trickle-down effect and how one missing ingredient can alter so many functions of the mind, body, and spirit. Feeding your body properly will boost your mood and abilities in ways you didn't expect.

The same is true for moving your body. Physical movement generates feel-good endorphins and hormones, but it's also necessary for moving energy that may be stuck in your body. It's very common to store emotions in the body. Like we touched upon already, if you've ever been so excited you could jump or so angry you wanted to punch something, you have a pretty good idea of what it's like to have so much emotion running through your body that you had to release it physically. Or if you've ever been in a yoga class and you started to cry or laugh or feel various sensations you couldn't explain after an intense pose, these are the extreme examples of energy moving through the body and how it feels to release them. There are also subtler ways this occurs, but unless you are paying close attention or are very in tune to your body, you might intellectually miss it. But it's still happening. It's always happening, and it's important for you to remember the necessity of these practices.

As well, it is important for you to understand all the factors that might be contributing to your mental health. Have you ever given any thought to how the music you listen to affects your brain's physiology? How do you feel after listening to heavy metal music? How about after classical music, light spa music, or sounds of nature? How about the way you feel after a 3-minute cold shower versus a 20-minute hot bath? How about after time spent with someone who is always positive, upbeat, and full of energy versus time spent with someone who constantly complains and talks about how difficult life is?

The lights you are exposed to also make a huge difference to your brain function. Full-spectrum lights (also dubbed "happy lights") emulate the sun and lift your mood, whereas generic fluorescent lights will affect you in a totally different way. This is why it is suggested to use full-spectrum lights in your house (or purchase a light box that uses full-spectrum lights) when you live in a state that doesn't get very much sunlight. Your body and brain are not only able to make certain nutrients when exposed to full-spectrum lighting (think vitamin D), but also psychological cues that lift your mood and send signals to the rest of the body, resulting in optimum health.

The sun is one of the many forces that set the rhythm of the earth and communicate to your mind and body how you should behave for optimum health. Think about the circadian rhythm and how sunlight affects your 24-hour wake and sleeping pattern. You are given physical, mental, and behavioral cues that follow the schedule of light and darkness. If you keep on track with the schedule set by the earth, you will be in the best situation possible for the greatest health and wellness.

Ancient Ayurvedic tradition suggests the most important times to sleep are from 10 pm to 2 am, and if sleep occurs during these hours, you will be sharper and better for it. There is a reason the sun rises and sets, and it sends signals to nearly every organism on Earth to wake up and go to sleep. Sleeping enough and at the hours intended by nature can majorly improve your health. Even though it is sometimes difficult in our modern society, this is 100% my experience, and I strongly believe it is wise to respect Mother Nature's cycle.

Learning to control the breath is another very important piece of brain health. Your breathing sends signals to the brain, telling it to relax or tense up. When your breath is short and quick, your body perceives a threat and gets ready for "fight or flight." This is very effective in a dangerous situation, but when done daily or hourly (as it often occurs in modern society) it can wreak havoc on your body and brain as it sends signals to secrete hormones that put stress on your system. Think about the biological need for the fight-or-flight syndrome. Thousands of years ago, when faced with a predator, let's say a tiger, you would need the hormone surge in the body, which gives your muscles immediate energy to run fast and far. This biological response shuts down other functions in the body (digestion, logical thinking, reproduction, growth, blood flow to the skin, the immune system, amongst others). The body is so intelligent, it knows the most important thing to maintain life at the moment is to run and run quickly!

This process is absolutely necessary and is still useful in today's society. The same fight-or-flight reaction kicks in if you are about to get hit by a car and need to get out of the way quickly. The problem is that your brain cannot differentiate between true imminent danger and a small perceived threat such as a report that is due to a boss and is not yet complete, a demanding email from a customer, a confrontational person on the road or in line next to you at a grocery store, or your child as she is misbehaving in public. The reactive mind cannot differentiate between these stressful situations, so people often go from situation to situation triggering the release of the stress hormone cortisol many times a day.

Cortisol sends signals to the body to prepare for fight or flight, shuts down all those important processes we need daily for optimum health (immune system, digestion, etc.), and also sends you signals to eat once the perceived stress is removed. Remember, the original intent of the process was a very demanding, physical fight or flight, which if actually used, would require major energy and calories to replace what was expended. You can see how this would perpetuate a nasty cycle, leading to weight gain, lessened happiness, and deteriorating health.

Knowing this, it is easier to see why they say all dis-ease starts with stress.

Even the words you use affect your brain's health. Learning to stay positive and find the good in all situations will greatly help boost your brain's power. There are many experiments where the subjects are instructed to say positive, upbeat things, and their bodies respond with better posture and more signs of health and vitality, while their minds respond with increased happiness and optimism. On the contrary, when the subject is asked to say negative things, their posture suffers by making them smaller with rounded shoulders, a closed heart chakra, and decreased signs of health and happiness. These types of experiments can easily be repeated on yourself, and you will notice that being happy and upbeat in your words increases your mind and body's energy and health, while being negative lowers your energy and health. The results are instantaneous. Try out the difference and see how it makes you feel:

Say out loud to yourself, "*You are smart, successful, energetic, loving, and loved.*" Take note of how you feel.

Then say, "*You are stupid, a failure, lazy, and no one loves you.*" Again, take note of how you feel.

Identify the internal dialogue you have with yourself and recognize how 24 hours a day of negative or positive internal talk is affecting your entire psyche. You may find your internal dialogue is a replication of the way your caregivers spoke to you when growing up. You typically internalize their voices as the "voice inside your head," which is ultimately the lens through which you see your life. This is why it is so important to clean up your words around your children. Fostering happy, healthy communication with them is essential if you want to give them a fighting chance at staying positive in the world they are growing up in. In order to be able to give this to your children, it is essential you begin to understand and acknowledge the level of happiness present in your own internal voices. Maybe it's time to retrain the voice in your mind to be more positive, which will bring you increased health and happiness.

The mind is a very important part of your physical health. It's nearly impossible to distinguish between the two. You may often hear of detoxification and think of doing a fast of some kind by eating certain foods that help you detox, but I challenge you to see that emotional and mental detox is just as important as physical or food detox. There are many ways to detox the mind, but none more powerful than meditation. We will get into the specifics of why meditation is so beneficial later in the book, as well as different meditations you might want to try. But in the meantime, you can start to keep close watch of the rituals in your life.

Whether you realize it or not, everything you do on a daily basis is a ritual. What are the rituals in your life that surround mental stimulants, food, movement, and detoxification? These rituals will help build a solid foundation of the mind or an unstable foundation. And the foundation of the mind eventually manifests into the physical, so these rituals will eventually control the fate of your health and life. Small upgrades to your rituals can do fantastic things for your mind, body, and spirit. Start noticing what you are doing to yourself with all you allow in your world. Maybe watch less violence on television or remove toxic people from your life. Maybe put a reminder on your phone to take ten deep breaths every hour. Maybe add probiotics into your morning routine. Just pick one small upgrade from this chapter and slowly start changing your life.

Chapter 4 Checklist

1. Consider your emotional shortcomings as a gift for growth and get excited about the opportunities they present.

2. Ask the five people closest to you what they would change about you if they could and seriously reflect on their answers.

3. Admit your areas for growth to your friends and family, asking for their help in correcting your issues.

- Don't forget to make apologies, if necessary.

4. Journal daily for five minutes.

- Write honestly how you feel and what comes to mind.
- Do not sensor so you can look for themes in your writing, which will suggest what type of internal dialogue you have.

5. Support your brain health and overall happiness by:

- Increasing your intake of fiber-rich, natural, and unprocessed foods.
- Cutting back on processed sugar.
- Adding a daily probiotic to your diet.
- Adding movement into your life.
- Using music to lift your mood.
- Spending more time with positive, uplifting people.
- Spending less time with negative, draining, or toxic people.
- Switching out the lights in your home to full spectrum lights or purchasing a light box.
- Getting ready for bed around 9 pm so you are asleep by 10 pm.
- Learning proper breathing or meditation techniques to deal with the fight-or-flight hormone, cortisol.
- Using more positive, uplifting words.

- Watching less violence and overall negativity on television or online.
- Adding a reminder on your calendar or phone to take a few deep breaths throughout the day.

Chapter 5

Body—The Body, The Vessel

Just as what you put into your mind has a profound effect on your mental health, what you put into your body and on your skin has a profound effect on your physical health. Food, water, air, lotions, soap, and other substances such as various types of inhalants (smoke) or drugs (including pharmaceuticals) have a profound effect on the state of dis-ease in your body. Everything you put into and on your body will fall into one of two categories: medicine or poison. You are either healing or harming your body every single time you put something in or on it. The skin is the largest organ on the body, and unlike in your digestive system, which has organs that help filter the toxins out, whatever is put on the skin is immediately absorbed into the body.

You may not realize pharmaceuticals could be poison to the body as well. Have you ever wondered why so many get recalled? Have you ever studied the testing process or approval process of a pharmaceutical drug? How long are studies? How many participants were involved in the trial? Who funded the study used to determine if the drug is safe? Is that study credible if the only study done was by the makers of the drugs? If the study tested the effects of taking a drug for six months and you are put on the drug for the rest of your life, do you realize that no one has studied the effect of that pill on humans for as long as you've been taking it? Are you volunteering to be the long-term study?

Have any studies been done on the exact combination of pharmaceuticals you are currently taking (if you are taking multiple drugs)?

This is why I always consider ancient and holistic remedies to treat any ailments before taking modern medicine's pharmaceuticals. Food, herbs, spices, and the like have been used to treat dis-ease for thousands of years. They are tried and true with no scary chemical toxins or unknown side effects. They may take longer to work (or they may not), but they work by balancing the body's natural system and allowing the body heal the issue versus just masking the problem. There are shamans and medicine men of indigenous societies who were so knowledgeable on the use of these ancient traditions that they cared for the body in a very different way than modern medicine does. Something happened in modern society where we stopped valuing natural remedies. The instant gratification of modern medicine took precedence over ancient healing traditions. However, I think now that we are looking back on what we have done, people are starting to consider natural remedies and be far more open-minded about this type of approach than ever before. We are starting to realize the error of our ways, and it seems many are now searching to go back to a more natural way of living.

Many whole foods, spices, and herbs are natural antibiotics, anti-inflammatories, and antibacterials, and also have so many micronutrients you need to be healthy. With consistent use of these foods in your everyday life, you are flooding the body with properties that will keep dis-ease at bay. When you eat the right foods, you'll get thousands of phytochemicals and micronutrients in your diet naturally For example, broccoli has over a thousand different nutrients in it, and a strawberry has over 700. Processed foods, even with added vitamins, cannot begin to compare to this. And if you have natural antibiotics in your diet at all times, your immune system will be strong enough to fight dis-ease before it takes root in your body, so you won't get sick and need manmade antibiotics to heal yourself. The same is true for antibacterial foods and especially true for anti-inflammatory foods. Your body is an astounding self-healing organism that is naturally resistant to dis-ease. It is designed to NOT get disease. It is designed to be RESISTANT to bacteria, viruses, and dis-ease.

Most Americans have a suppressed immune system due to the Standard American Diet (SAD) they consume. Most people are not getting a significant amount of vitamins, minerals, antioxidants, or phytochemicals, which are all types of micronutrients. Dr. Joel Furhman, a family physician, *New York Times* best-selling author, and nutritional researcher who specializes in preventing and reversing disease through nutritional and natural methods, was one of the many guest teachers at a school I attended—The Institute for Integrated Nutrition. In one of our lectures, he stated that the average American needs to increase the quantity of their micronutrient intake by about ten to fifteen times to have optimal immune function and avoid dis-ease. There are so many examples of foods that can help you stay healthy; the list is endless. There are also many foods that help with specific ailments, but for the sake of a good overview, I will focus on some foods that will help increase your immunity, because improving your immune system will help you stay strong and resilient to dis-ease.

When antioxidants are missing in the body, viruses replicate. But when the immune system is functioning optimally, meaning the person is consuming all the micronutrients necessary, viruses are significantly reduced and have a difficult time replicating. Antioxidants that assist in this are found in most natural, unprocessed foods, but specifically in berries, grapes, nuts, dark green vegetables, beans, and cacao (which is the main ingredient in chocolate). In addition to the antioxidants, there are also numerous benefits in many superfoods, including avocados, beets, broccoli, Brussel sprouts, cabbage, cauliflower, coconut, peppers, garlic, maca, pomegranates, spirulina, goji berries, mulberries, chia seeds, flax seeds, and hemp seeds.

Dr. Furhman teaches that eating more vegetables, specifically green vegetables, will help you repair your DNA and protect you from cancer. The fewer green vegetables you eat, the higher your susceptibility to cancer. And green cruciferous vegetables, like cabbage, broccoli, kale, and bok choy, arm the body with the ability to reduce the effect of early life damage to the cells. Dr. Fuhrman also discusses studies where high levels of raw green vegetables were given to women with the breast cancer gene and the gene was suppressed. Even colon cancer was suppressed with a diet high in vegetables. Those without the cancer gene see a 50%–60% reduction in colon cancer when eating a diet high in cruciferous vegetables. Dr. Fuhrman has many, many books that are easy to find that give diets and meal plans based on these principles.

Eating green vegetables on a regular basis activates your natural protective mechanism against cancer. Humans are a green-vegetable-dependent animal. You MUST eat your greens. If you're not eating green vegetables, this protective mechanism isn't activated. This could possibly be the most important upgrade to your diet available.

Dr. Furhman reiterates in lecture that you must not only eat your greens, but you must CHEW your greens. Chewing your food THOROUGHLY is one of the keys to getting all the nutritional properties out of them. When you chew your food, specifically vegetables, you break open the cell walls of the vegetables and get into the cell membrane where important chemicals and enzymes are located. The chewing of the vegetable allows the enzyme to transform the chemical into various anti-cancer elements that can be utilized by your body. The anti-cancer elements are not available until the vegetable is chewed. The enzyme has to be exposed to the chemical in order to become an anti-cancer element. So, if you don't chew very well, you're not getting the anti-cancer compounds. As well, there are bacteria and enzymes in your mouth that mix with the newly formed anti-cancer compound that create even more chemicals and compounds that help improve your immunity in various ways in your body. Blending these vegetables in a smoothie does the same thing as chewing, so you are covered when making green smoothies.

Each vegetable has different enzymes, chemicals, and compounds created when blended or chewed. So don't get in a rut of eating just one type of vegetable and think you are covered. Eat as many different types as possible, in as many different ways as possible. Blend them, juice them, cook them, and eat them raw. The more ways you prepare them and the more types you eat, the more you are covered.

Dr. Furhman also indicates that mushrooms should be added to your diet. They are fundamental to your immune system's optimal performance because of their cancer preventing mechanisms. They play a very important role in the body of binding to abnormal cells, which activates the body's defenses, calling the immune system into action. Mushrooms bind to these damaged cells so they are identified and removed quickly by your body.

Mushrooms also keep the levels of estrogen down, which decreases the acceleration of cancer in women. Eating ten grams of mushrooms daily, which is only one white button mushroom, reduces breast cancer rates significantly. Studies have shown that women who ate green vegetables, green tea, and mushrooms daily had astronomical reductions in breast cancer rates. Mushrooms, greens, onions, garlic, beans, berries, and cinnamon are all foods that inhibit the growth of the blood vessels that feed the growth of fat and cancer cells in the body. Onions and tomatoes are other cancer-fighting champions that cannot go without mention. Tomatoes contain something called lycopene that is only released when cooked; therefore, it is important to eat tomatoes both cooked (so the lycopene can be released) and raw so the other properties of the tomato can be utilized. Again, vary the vegetables and the way you prepare them to be fully covered nutritionally.

Another thing to think about is how many animal products you are eating. Studies show that as your intake increases, so do certain cancer risks. You might want to think about lowering your intake if your diet consists of meat at every meal. I'm not advocating everyone become a vegetarian or vegan, but I am encouraging you to look at how much animal-based food you are eating and make a conscious decision to learn more about the meat you consume. Is it farm-raised, hormone-free, and antibiotic-free? Remember you are only as clean as what your food eats. If we are trying to lessen the toxins and chemicals coming into our body, we need to be conscious of what the animals we eat are eating.

There are many scientific studies on the benefits of natural, whole, unprocessed foods on the body to prevent disease and reverse damage. Consider incorporating these healing foods into your diet. You want to eat foods that have high micronutrient and antioxidant levels, foods that are rich in anti-cancer compound—healthy foods (green vegetables, mushrooms, berries, nuts, seeds, onions, superfoods)—and REALLY limit the bad stuff (the processed foods, the animal products). Eat a variety of vegetables prepared a variety of ways, and remember to CHEW YOUR FOOD for optimal health. These little upgrades every day will make a HUGE impact on your health!

As important as food is for your body's health, moving your body is just as important. We've already talked about how energy can get stuck in the body, but movement also helps with physical conditions such as blood flow, increasing HDL (the good cholesterol), decreasing the risk of cardiovascular disease, as well as preventing a wide range of health conditions, including stroke, metabolic conditions, type 2 diabetes, depression, and certain types of cancer. Movement improves mood, boosts energy, and promotes better sleep.

If all that wasn't enough, movement also helps us detoxify, which might just be the most important attribute of all. The most obvious form of detoxification is sweating, which removes impurities from the body. This is why you want to promote perspiration instead of stopping it. The idea of using antiperspirant is so backward when the goal is improving health.

The body has a wonderful, natural detoxification system built in that you are trying to stop when using antiperspirant.

In addition to sweating, when you move the body in certain ways, you help the organs detoxify. This is why yoga is considered a detoxification method. When doing yoga, you put your body in positions that ring out your organs and help remove impurities. Yoga systematically stretches and compresses every part of the body, which makes it well suited for removing waste, like carbon dioxide, lactic acid, and lymphatic fluid from the deep tissues and extremities of the body. The yogic breath also plays a significant role in detox. Shallow breathing doesn't allow fresh oxygen to flood the body, nor does it allow you to expel hazardous carbon dioxide from lung tissue or stimulate the digestive organs.

The three main systems of the body that help with detoxification are the lymphatic, digestive, and circulatory systems. The lymph system collects fluid from all over the body and transports it to the lymph nodes where harmful contaminants, like bacteria, are removed before the lymphatic fluid is returned to the bloodstream. The digestive system processes food you eat, separating nutrients from waste, which is then eliminated from the body. The circulatory system pumps blood through the body, delivering oxygen to the cells while carrying waste products away from them. This robust system works very well on its own, but with heavy demands on the body, high stress levels, and poor nutrition, you can assist the body with other helpful detoxification processes.

A few ways you can help your body to detox besides movement are dry brushing, oil pulling, proper sleep, taking detoxifying foods and herbs, spending time in saunas, jumping on a rebounder, bathing in detox mixtures, hot/cold hydrotherapy, colonics, and detox body and foot spas. Let's start with the detoxing that helps the lymphatic system. The first is dry brushing. This task takes about two minutes, and there are specific brushes you can buy online or at certain health stores that cost about $10; these brushes have hard bristles and are made especially for dry body brushing. You literally brush your body to activate the lymph system with this brush. This should always be done from the ends of the extremities towards the heart. So, for example, brush from the tips of your fingers, up your arm, towards your heart. Brush from the bottoms of your feet, towards your ankle, then knee, beyond the hip, up your mid-section, towards your heart. Do this through your entire body and, women especially, be extra careful to brush around the chest area and under the armpits. Wearing restrictive underwire bras makes the lymph fluid extremely sluggish. Dry brushing helps the lymph system move waste to be processed and removed by your body.

Another way to assist the lymphatic system is to jump on a trampoline. For women, this is best done without a bra so the chest area can gain maximum movement. A rebounder is a mini-trampoline that can be purchased online from certain sport stores for sometimes under $100. There are even foldable ones that can easily slip under a bed or in a closet when not in use. Jumping helps the lymphatic system move and process toxins effectively and efficiently.

Alternating hot and cold hydrotherapy is another effective way to get the lymph system moving. This is as easy as turning your shower water to cold for a few minutes while taking a warm shower. Start with 30 to 60 seconds of cold water, and as you are able, increase that time to 2 or more minutes. This shock of cold water will invigorate your lymph system and get things moving, in addition to stimulating your mind and waking you up. It takes a bit of getting used to, but it is a very rewarding practice. In certain bathhouses and spas, you can find hot and cold water baths and spend half a day relaxing and rejuvenating the body, mind, and spirit. Some of them even have saltwater baths, which are very effective in removing impurities from the skin. If you are interested in a bathhouse, they are easily searched on the internet with keywords like "European bath houses" or "bath house detox" along with your city and state's name.

Next is what some might argue is the most important ritual of all: sleep. When you sleep, your body rejuvenates and repairs itself. Your digestion is shut down, which is what takes up most of your energy during waking hours. Your brain is in sleep mode. Your body goes to work and spends energy on healing the body and detoxifying harmful substances from your system. This is why you might find that you sweat while sleeping, because the body is eliminating harmful substances. This is especially true after a night of drinking alcohol. Be sure to get enough sleep, especially after ingesting harmful substances.

Spending time in a sauna is another fabulous detoxification practice. There are many types of saunas, and all are beneficial. One that is well known and extremely effective for detox is called an "infrared sauna." This type of sauna uses infrared technology to penetrate deep into the body and assist with detoxification. There are home units that can be purchased for a few thousand dollars for a new unit. I found mine used online for $250. If you research your brands and know what you are looking for, used units can often be found online for a portion of the original price. You can also find spas or centers in your area that let you rent the sauna by the hour. This is a great way to get a sauna treatment, maybe once a month or even weekly, for minimal cost.

The mouth has many toxins in it, as morning breath often implies. In addition to brushing your teeth, scraping the tongue and oil pulling are both wonderful tools to assist in mouth detox. A tongue scraper can be purchased for under $5 from most health stores, and this allows you to scrape away substances that build up on the back of the tongue. In addition, the ancient practice of oil pulling will help you reduce the toxins in your mouth. Put a tablespoon or a small swig of cold-pressed organic oil into your mouth and swish around for at least 2 minutes or up to 15 minutes. Be sure to spit this oil out after you are done. (You do not want to swallow all the toxins you just pulled out of your mouth.) You literally use oil that you would use in your kitchen in this process. I typically keep the oil in my shower and take a quick swig before I shower. As I shower I swish, and when I get out of the shower, I spit it in my toilet and flush. Voila!

The colon, or large intestine, is the organ in the body that is responsible for absorbing water and dumping waste in the form of feces. Despite our society's awkwardness when it comes to the discussion of waste elimination, it's a very important function that helps tremendously with detoxification. Before humans started eating processed foods and drinking too little water, the colon functioned more optimally. Now it's quite helpful to assist your colon's waste elimination. Two of the best ways to do this are to eat as much fiber as possible and get regular colonics (monthly or quarterly).

Waste can build up in the walls of the colon or in the pocket-like spaces in its lining. Colonics use water to flush the organ and remove this waste. There are two types of colonics: open and closed loop systems. Open colonic systems are questionable in safety and effectiveness. They use a hard plastic tube that resembles a hose that pumps water into the colon, while simultaneously letting the water flow out of the colon. The effectiveness is questionable because the colon is never truly filled with water, opening the pocket-like spaces for collected waste to be eliminated. The safety is questionable because the tube used in an open system could potentially perforate the colon.

On the contrary, a closed colonic system is far more reliable, safe, and effective. A closed system plugs the opening to the colon, allowing for the colon to be blown up like a balloon with water, which opens the pocket-like spaces in the colon's lining, eliminating any waste that has collected in these pockets. The hose used to deliver the water in the closed system is a solid, rounded plastic end, making insertion easy and more comfortable, and also reducing the chance for perforation.

Detoxifying foods and herbs are another wonderful way to detoxify the body on a daily basis. Green vegetables are very effective in detoxification, as are most whole, natural, unprocessed foods. We've touched upon food in a major way in this chapter, but the topic of detoxifying foods could warrant a book of its own, so we will keep it to eating a well-rounded, natural diet in order to detoxify the body. The body will start detoxifying from the chemicals and additives in processed food if the processed foods are eliminated. This, along with feeding the body proper nutrients, will allow for a slow and comfortable detox process.

Chapter 5 Checklist

Look at everything you put in or on your body and identify which category it falls into: medicine or poison.

1. Check the ingredient lists of everything you use on your skin:

- Face and body soap
- Masks, creams, or anything else you put on your face
- Shampoo and conditioner
- Sunscreens
- Bug sprays
- Make up

2. Replace toxic products that contain chemicals with natural products as your current inventory is depleted (if it is too expensive to wipe things out and start over, that is).

3. If you use water filters for drinking water but do not for your shower, consider adding a shower filter.

4. Consider and research holistic remedies for everyday ailments.

5. Add natural antibiotic, anti-inflammatory, and antibacterial foods, herbs, and spices into your diet to avoid getting sick in the first place.

6. Improve your immune system by using the following natural, unprocessed foods in your diet:

- Berries
- Grapes
- Nuts
- Dark green vegetables
- Kale
- Bok Choy
- Beans
- Cacao (main ingredient in dark chocolate!)
- Avocados

- Beats
- Broccoli
- Brussel sprouts
- Cabbage
- Cauliflower
- Coconut
- Peppers
- Garlic
- Maca
- Pomegranates
- Spirulina
- Goji berries
- Mulberries
- Chia seeds
- Flax seeds
- Hemp seeds
- Mushrooms
- Cinnamon
- Green tea
- Onions
- Beans
- Tomatoes (cooked & raw)
- Nuts

7. Chew your food (specifically vegetables) thoroughly.

8. Eat a wide variety of fruits and vegetables.

- Eat as many colors of natural foods as possible (the nutrients in food designate their color, so if you eat all the colors of the rainbow daily, you are eating a well-rounded diet full of all nutrients).

9. Shop for the following when you do eat meat:

- Farm Raised
- Hormone-Free
- Antibiotic-Free

10. Consider lessening the amount of meat in your diet.

- Swap out meals to a healthier version of the same animal product.
- Switch a meal a week from red meat to white meat.
- Switch a meal a week from white meat to fish.
- Switch a meal a week from fish to plant-based.

11. Add detoxification into your life naturally by:

- Moving your body with exercise, yoga, or just walking more
- Deep breathing
- Sweating more often
  - Exercise
  - Sauna
  - Outdoors in heat
- Dry brushing
- Oil pulling
- Tongue scraper
- Proper sleep (7+ hours of sleep/night)
- Adding detoxifying herbs into your diet
- Jumping on a rebounder (small trampoline)
- Using detox baths or foot spas
- Getting colonics
- Using hot/cold hydrotherapy
- Eating more fiber

Chapter 6

Spirit—Let Spirit In

People can often get really worked up, uptight, or skeptical when the conversation of spirituality begins. Rightfully so, as the topic addresses many very important aspects of most belief systems. Family roots, community groups, organized religion, the shaping of your personality and character, your ideas of good/bad/right/wrong, and so much more play a role in this idea of spirituality.

Spirituality is a very personal journey. Even defining it can get difficult. When thinking of my spirituality, I am looking to answer the following questions: How do I define my connection with the infinite? How does this relate to a God, or maybe many gods? Is this the same as a higher power or maybe my higher power or source power? Can the ideas of God and the Universe be used interchangeably? What does the afterlife look like, if it's even a possibility? How does the concept of karma work into all this? How about reincarnation? If there is reincarnation, do we always reincarnate to Earth, or might there be graduate planets? Is there just one truth, or are there endless truths? Is it possible to believe in portions of various religions, or must a religion in its totality define what I believe? And so on, and so on, and so on.

My point is that whatever your terminology, whatever your opinions, whatever your (religious) beliefs, the idea of your spirituality is usually a very personal connection to something or someone that is larger than you. We are usually referring to a power that is beyond us that helps measure meaning in our lives. We typically tie this to certain customs or practices, like attending ceremonies in a church, synagogue, temple, ashram, monastery, or possibly a classroom. There are many ways humans define their spiritually, from religions to lifestyles, gurus to gods, meditation to prayer.

It's my opinion that it makes no difference what you call it or even how you define it. All that matters is that you let it in and keep communication open to allow it into your world. Letting spirit into your life might be the most rewarding and life-altering thing you can do for your mind and body. Spirit connects you to something larger. It connects you to a higher version of yourself and absolutely helps you to become the best version of yourself.

The allowing of spirit into one's life happens differently for each of us. For some, it's through organized institutions and doctrines. For others, it's sitting silently in meditation, listening for the answers. Maybe it's a practice of doing good deeds for others or being charitable. No two people, even within the same organized religion, will experience spirituality in the same way. So maybe it's time we give each other a break and let everyone think and feel however they want to about this very personal subject of spirituality.

I was raised in a Catholic family. I went to private schools, even an all-girl Catholic high school. My religious upbringing was strict and, for various reasons, never really resonated with me. I never felt like Catholicism was MY personal belief system. It was something I was born into. I found more fault with it than I did comfort. Maybe it was the people teaching it to me. Maybe it was because it was presented to me as a tool of control rather than a channel of support. Maybe I just had an enormous chip on my shoulder and hated the world. Actually, yes, that was it. No religion would have helped me back then. I was a confused teenage girl, living in a very turbulent environment with little emotional support, begging (in all the wrong ways) for love. It's no wonder religion couldn't get through to me, even when drinking it from a fire hose. I was lost. I was emotionally tortured. I was an absolute mess. And it wasn't until I found my own version of spirituality later in life that I finally learned how to open communication with MY personal belief system.

After many years of self-abuse in the form of awful eating (taking in absolutely no real nutrition), very little physical movement, and heavy drug and alcohol use, my body FINALLY broke down. I was admitted to the hospital after a major surgery. I had a large tumor removed from my colon, as well as much of the colon itself, many feet of my small intestine, and my appendix. Next was a life-changing diagnosis of Crohn's disease. Recovering from a very traumatic surgery, my broken body was finally on the mend, but my newly broken mind was just starting on its journey of recovery.

I was a mess. I cried and I cried, sometimes for hours on end. Not only was I healing some serious physical wounds, I was also, for the first time in my life, starting to deal with a newly broken mind and previously broken spirit. I had no idea how much I had self-medicated my entire life. When I stopped the drugs, the alcohol, the partying, and the distractions, I saw for the first time who was left: Cassie Sobelton. And I wasn't sure who she was. I was confused. I was disoriented. I wasn't sure what I believed or how I was going to move forward.

I was told I was very ill. I didn't like that. I was told I had an incurable disease. I didn't like that either. I was told I would have to take a ridiculous number of prescription medications for the rest of my life. I hated that, although I wasn't even sure yet why. I was confused for the first time in my life. I was scared, seriously scared. I was seeing things clearly for the first time since I started the numbing-out practice that I had developed as a teenager out of self-preservation. I was dealing with many years of repressed thoughts, pain, and emotions that were just making their way to the surface.

Knowing what you now do about chakras, healing, and how your emotional issues correspond to illnesses, can you see what was going on with me? Can you see how unresolved 1st and 2nd chakra issues manifested in my body? Actually, they were with me my entire life, but much quieter and easier to push down and ignore. My mom tells me that my digestive symptoms started as an infant, but I remember them from early childhood years. I especially remember them in high school. I did seek out medical help, but after the third doctor told me it was nothing or it would eventually go away, I finally just gave up hope. This coincided with me giving up hope in many ways, although it was really no coincidence.

I was in high school. I was a major troublemaker. I had a stormy, unstructured upbringing. I didn't have much parental supervision or support. So, go figure, I found drugs. And they really helped me. They helped me feel good again. They helped me numb out from all the pain that was happening around me. They helped me feel less alone. But the unexpected side effect was that they helped me feel less of everything. I felt less pain, sorrow, and loneliness, but also less joy, happiness, love, and fulfillment. I had completely cut myself off from everything. Everything good and everything bad was beyond my reach. I was numb. And I thought it felt good, but really, it just felt better than horrible.

My surgery forced the detoxification and rehabilitation of my life. I left that hospital and made a serious decision about where my life was headed. The feelings and experiences I went through in that hospital and during the months that followed were fuel for a new beginning. I let myself feel again. I felt so much emotion, I could barely handle it. I cried more in the months following that surgery than I did in my entire life, sometimes for hours on end. I let everything out!

The dreams I had during this time were astonishing. The insights I had were more than remarkable. For the first time in my entire life, I was cleaning the dirty windshield of my soul. And when I could finally see inside again, I saw a remarkable spirit inside of me. I learned a big life lesson about how a piece of God comes into this world with us at birth and stays with us until we leave this earth. It's our job to make sure we don't muddy the window to our soul, thus keeping the connection strong in order to live a life filled with spirit.

Many would say I am a stubborn gal and, par for the course, it took a major illness and set of surgeries for me to have that windshield cleaned clear enough for me to recognize that spirit lives inside of me. It doesn't have to be this tough, though. When I look back on it, I was given this opportunity more times than I could count. I had so many injuries, accidents, and illnesses in my life prior to my surgeries. They were all less severe, but as I see it now, they were increasingly more severe each time, almost as if spirit was trying to show me the lesson in the easiest way possible. When I didn't listen, it was increased in severity. When I didn't listen again, the volume was turned up. Again and again and again.

But the important part is that I finally listened. I finally heard spirit, loud and clear. And now I realize my goal in life is to let my light shine. My goal is to keep the windshield clean so spirit can shine and work through me. But I also realize how I muddied my windshield. I realize that American society has a way of throwing dirt on our windshields. We live in a society that completely debunks this type of thinking, talking, or believing. We live in a society that values everything except this connection to spirit and, because of this, it's difficult to stay focused on the integration of spirituality in our lives. We must make a conscious effort to stay connected to our true self, to our inner spirit. Our society does not value this. Our society does not help us achieve mind-body-spirit balance. If we want balance, we need to find ways to strengthen this connection on an hourly, daily, weekly, monthly, and annual basis. It's the least we can do if we want to succeed.

If you feel like you could benefit from more spirituality in your life or feel like your connection to spirit isn't that strong right now, there are many things you can do to help that. One of the best things you can do is check in with yourself about the issue. I enjoy checking in with myself often on various topics. It takes a little practice to trust yourself, but is very easy to do. Find a comfortable spot, close your eyes, take a few deep breaths, and relax. Once you are relaxed, ask yourself what would be helpful for you to connect with spirit. You might get an answer that meditation would be beneficial, attending a prayer group, talking to your guardian angel, volunteering to help others in need, spiritual or life coach counseling, a daily practice of gratitude, a weekly massage, learning a new sport, taking up yoga, walks in nature, reading a new book; the list is endless! We will go into detail in the next chapter about a few of these things, but what is important is that you find something and pursue it.

Spirit will not intrude on your life. Spirit is waiting patiently for you to ask. Spirit is all-supportive and gives you complete control. Spirit is hoping that you will call out. Spirit is ready to take your hand, but you must offer up it up for spirit to take it.

There are very few things I will tell you to do that are extreme, but I am going to break my own rule here and tell you to attend, if at all possible, a spiritual retreat. Some of you may be coming off lifetimes of ignoring and repressing spirit. (This is obvious with all the illness in our society, yes?) Since spirit can be very subtle and some of you may have added layers of mud and grime over it, I believe a reset is necessary. Often a retreat will give you the reset you need in a very safe and loving environment.

Retreats come in all shapes and sizes. Retreats range in length, but the typical durations include a weekend retreat, a 7–10 day retreat, a month, or even a three-month-long retreat. They can be held in any country imaginable and any setting possible. I've seen them held on beaches, mountains, huts, tents, or in the wilderness. I've seen them held at monasteries, churches, hotels, spas, and homes. They're often set off the grid, giving you the rare opportunity to realize how easily we can live in harmony with nature and without our ubiquitous technology. This is a very unique experience, for Americans especially.

I've been to more retreats than I can count, and each one has been fabulous in its own right. However, the most life-changing retreats, the ones where I have grown the most, are those that completely submerge me into a new lifestyle. Typically, these retreats are for a week or longer. This amount of time allows you to honestly experience what authentic spiritual living will do to/for you. If in one week (just seven days) you can get to a place of joy, happiness, or maybe even bliss, can you even imagine what a life devoted to this way of living could allow for?

Right now, however, most people cannot live this way. Right now, you are a spiritual being living in a modern world. You may have a spouse or children or a career and obligations. You might not be able—or even want—to leave your life, career, or loved ones and go live a life of spiritual devotion, no matter how much bliss it might bring you. So how can you incorporate spirituality into your modern, everyday life? How do you meld what you might learn on retreat and what you currently live in your "real life," so you can be the BEST person possible in this life you are living?

The only way I have found to integrate these two worlds successfully (at least at the beginning) is to completely immerse myself in it so that I can create new spiritual practices and habits to bring back to my normal life. And I feel the same would be true for anyone reading this. This is why I feel so strongly that retreating is necessary.

When you go on retreat, you learn new practices and develop new habits, even in as little as a week. Once developed, these habits are much easier to bring back and incorporate into your former life, thus slowly changing your old life into something new and healthier. Just like you learned habits slowly throughout your entire life that make up your current lifestyle, in the same way you start to learn new habits and start turning your life around. After each retreat, you might bring home one or two new habits, but the seeds are planted for many other habits that might later grow. If you can do this once or twice a year, your life will start to transform itself. It's inevitable.

When the retreat bug hit me, I had no exposure to retreats or even knew they existed. I was lost, and I was searching for something new. Within two weeks, three different people mentioned a life-changing retreat at a Buddhist Monastery in

Murphys, California. I looked online and found a place called the Zen Monastery Peace Center that offered retreats. There was very little detail about the retreat online, but I knew I was drawn to this retreat for a reason. I applied online that minute and went on an experience of a lifetime a few short weeks later.

Nothing in my entire life has been more transformational. Since then, I have been on many retreats. I make a practice of not looking into them in too much depth, as the experience of not knowing has proven to be heart opening for me. I have grown more in a week on retreat than in a decade living my "normal" American lifestyle. I have met friends who touched my soul in ways that are indescribable. I have fallen in love on retreat, deeply in love with men, with women, with places, and with ideas. I have yet to leave a retreat without tears of gratitude for what I experienced and what I learned. I still tear up at the thought. The beautiful souls, the devoted teachers, the safe space they hold for the rest of us to come experience our truth and dive deep into our emotional bodies with the love and support necessary to do such difficult work is nothing short of miraculous and godly.

And to think, if I had ignored the three "random" mentions of a retreat in Murphys, California, where might I be today? Was that a coincidence or a random act of spirit? There are times in my life when I would have dismissed that as a coincidence, but now I see them as signposts. I see spirit working through synchronicity to guide me to my next venture. I see coincidences as anything but. I see doors opening as an obvious sign to look inside, and sometimes that means walking away from something else that I thought for sure I was supposed to do.

I challenge you to put your antenna up. Can you start listening and watching to where spirit might be guiding you? Maybe you'll notice a few ads or verbal mentions of a retreat shortly after reading this. Maybe you'll notice a new class in your area that you've always wanted to take. Maybe you'll keep running into someone in your town that you feel drawn to introduce yourself to. Maybe you'll get a job offer in a new field that excites and interests you. The opportunities are limitless, and if you start watching closely, you just might notice spirit's signposts in your life. I urge you to follow them and watch your life unfold in magical ways.

Chapter 6 Checklist

1. Be open to new ways to let spirit into your life.

- Learn meditation
- Attend a (new) religious ceremony
- Practice prayer
- Practice visualization
- Look for opportunities to assist others with various good deeds
- Donate time or money to charity
- Learn to communicate with your guardian angels or spirit that surrounds you

2. Look for ways spirit might be trying to communicate with you.

- An incurable dis-ease
- Illnesses
- Injuries or accident

3. Listen for what spirit might be trying to tell you.

4. Identify ways you might be numbing out or pushing spirit away.

5. Set up your life to reinforce the mind-body-spirit connection.

6. Appreciate "random" coincidences as acts of spirit and follow the message.

7. Consider attending a spiritual retreat, especially if signs for this show up in your experiences.

Chapter 7

How to Attract Your Dream Life

The Law of Attraction has become a very popular term in the last decade. The movie *The Secret* brought this idea to the mainstream, and since then, it's been a topic of many books, talk shows, new age institutions, and philosophy. When I first heard of it, unlike most new age concepts that I had to warm up to, it instantly resonated with me. It made so much sense, and I saw how it had played out in my life thus far. I started thinking back on all the times I really wanted something to happen, how I used to daydream about it, and how it would then happen, many times against all odds. Then I thought of all the times I worried about something (sometimes unfounded) and how those situations always happened too. And lastly, I remembered all the times I ignored or refused to deal with situations (thus, giving them no energy) and how they always seemed to resolve themselves without me having to deal with them.

I've now been studying the Law of Attraction for about a decade, mostly through the books and teachings of Abraham Hicks (Jerry and Ester Hicks). I am absolutely certain of the law's existence and how it is working every single minute of every single day, with or without our belief or understanding. Just like the laws of gravity, motion, or relativity were always happening, even before they were "discovered" by humanity. When you drop an object, it will still fall to the ground even if you don't believe in gravity. Belief in this law does not change the outcome. If you don't understand gravity, you aren't any less susceptible to its effect—you don't fly off the earth while those who understand the law stay put. It just doesn't work this way. It's a law and it is happening always, regardless of your belief system.

Like all laws, the Law of Attraction is always in action. It has been since the day you were born and will continue to be until the last breath you take. What you are living right now is an accumulation of what you've attracted into your life so far. This includes your financial, mental, physical, and emotional situations, as well as your relationships. But it's not as cut-and-dried as it appears on the surface. What you attract is a match to very deep programming that you have learned through heavy social interacting and programming with the people and experiences around you. And for that reason, I don't think reciting a mantra, such as, "Money flows abundantly and effortlessly to me," works very well. It's a great concept, and I love the intention behind it, but could saying those seven words every morning really undo the deep programming that has occurred in someone who was born into a situation that taught them it was impossible to gain financial momentum in this world?

Think about someone who was raised by two parents who struggled financially their entire lives, both working multiple jobs for minimum wage and barely able to make ends meet. Think about the deep emotional programming that child has learned about money, through no "fault" of either his parents or himself. He watched his two wonderful, honest, loving parents struggle his entire life, trying to get ahead. He heard them talk about how hard it was to make money and was often told he had better learn to live frugally, as "money doesn't grow on trees." He watched them work themselves to death and leave this earth with very little financially to show for all their efforts. What do you think that boy will grow up believing about his ability to get ahead financially? Might he think it's useless and impossible? Might he have a deep-rooted belief that even with hard work, it's impossible to break through the glass ceiling of American wealth?

Do you think he could ever truly believe in his ability to attain financial abundance based on the programming and experiences he had so far in his life?

On the other hand, let's look at a child who was raised in a very wealthy family. The family had multiple homes around the country, country club memberships galore, private jets, yachts, and staff at their disposal. This child is always around money and wealthy people, thus, he thinks this is normal. Mom was always home, and the child was well traveled and never wanted for anything. This child thinks money does, in fact, grow on trees, as for him it almost does. His parents lightheartedly refer to him as a "mogul in training," and he is taught from a very young age that the world is his oyster. Again, no "fault" of anyone involved, but this child's experience is very different than the previous example. How do you think this child will relate to money when he grows up? Might he have a different relationship to money than the boy in the previous experience? What do you think his deep belief around money will be, and how will that play out in his life?

Do you see how early our programming starts and how deep it runs? Is it possible that saying an affirmation every morning, such as, "Money flows abundantly and effortlessly to me," could reverse this type of programming? Many of the Law of Attraction experts out there say it could, and I agree, it COULD. But most likely, it won't. The truth is you need to get deep down into your programming if you want to change deep beliefs that create your point of attraction. It's typically not as easy as saying a seven-word affirmation every morning. However, it IS possible and certainly won't hurt.

One of the biggest things you can do to start attracting better things into your life is to practice gratitude. Choosing to focus on gratitude will increase your awareness of good things around you, which will help attract more good things into your experience. Rather than trying to fight your programming, gratitude helps you to shift that old program to a new program that expects things to happen that will make you feel grateful.

For example, what if the first boy (who was programmed to believe that finances are hardships) started feeling gratitude for everything in his life that was given to him? What if he started a journal of gratitude every morning where he wrote down everything he felt gratitude for? The list might look something like this: I'm grateful for... the bedroom I rent in this apartment that keeps me safe from the elements, the food I eat to keep me nourished, the bus I take to work that keeps me warm in my commute and allows me to find a job farther away than I could walk, the clothes/jacket/gloves/hat I wear that keep me warm, the piece of gum my coworker gave me today, the paycheck my boss gave me so I can buy things I need, the stranger on the bus today who smiled at me and showed kindness.

As time goes on, that list gets easier and easier to write. And each thing he shows gratitude for will show up more prominently in his life. Showing gratitude for his paycheck could easily manifest a raise. All of the sudden, the man's boss comes to him and offers him a shift leader position at a $2/hour increase. Maybe strangers will start to not only smile at him, but strike up random conversations. Maybe one of those strangers owns a company and needs some help, so he offers him a job that pays more and is more exciting, fulfilling, and fun. Maybe the gratitude for the piece of gum he was given attracts more gifts into his life, and in the next week, his housemate gets a new bike and offers him his old bike. Maybe being thankful for a warm ride to work attracts him a coworker that lives close to him and asks if he would like to carpool for free,. The list goes on and on of possible manifestations of grateful thinking.

The gratitude journal will continue to be upgraded because he keeps feeling gratitude, which brings more things to be grateful for. Eventually, he has a bit of a skip in his step and is truly thinking, "Wow, things are really turning around for me. I can't believe what great luck I've been having lately." As he keeps positive and reinforces this feeling of good things coming to him, more of it will materialize in his life until one day, he's making double the money he was, living in his own place, driving his own car to work, has disposable income to buy what he needs, and he thinks, "Money flows abundantly and effortlessly to me, this is great!" And BAM!! There it is. He is finally living in a positive place in regard to finances. He changed his belief system around money and feels the difference. He might not even know what he has done. He might just think he finally got lucky. He might give all the credit to the boss who gave him a chance. Again, if you believe in it or not, if you understand it or not, the Law of Attraction is always working.

This example is about finances, but it works with anything in life. Starting a gratitude journal is a fabulous practice I urge you to begin immediately. Your gratitude list might be difficult to write at first because gratitude is a muscle you need to strengthen. At first, it can feel "fake" to write down things you are grateful for when you are not truly grateful, but once you get used to it, you will realize you have so much to be thankful for, and the list will be hard to stop. And the more you focus on gratitude, the more you will have to be grateful for and the more will flow into your life.

Just as you attract things for which to be grateful when you focus on gratitude, you also attract things you don't want when you focus on them—things like pain, suffering, illness, sadness, loneliness, anger, worry, stress, fear, and all the others you could be experiencing. These feelings are enhanced when you focus on them, talk about them, and give them energy. By flexing the muscle (focusing on and talking about the things that make you feel this way), you attract more things that will make you feel this way.

So, for example, if the man in the example above is stressed about not having enough money, he is putting an attraction point into the Universe of being stressed over not having enough money. Now he will attract things to make him feel more of that feeling (of not having enough). He will soon find he has manifested more and more ways to feel like he doesn't have enough money. His rent might be raised. His car might break down. His employer might go out of business, or he might be unfairly fired from his job, losing his income completely.

If you feel anger and focus on it, rather than learning techniques to let it go, you will attract more things to be angry about. You will find your way into traffic jams. You will attract people to cut you off on the road. You will attract argumentative people into your experience. You will find that people who are normally polite and agreeable will start to give you reasons to be angry with them. This is the case with anything you focus on, not just financial issues or anger. Anything you focus on becomes magnified.

If you've ever experienced any of these feelings, you know they're not always easy to find your way out of. We've already discussed gratitude and keeping a gratitude journal to help change your life. Another great way to turn things around is through the power of positive thinking, which many refer to as positive psychology. Your mind exaggerates that on which you focus, so you might as well focus on positive things, such as gratitude, trust, love, happiness, and all the other things that make you feel good.

An example of this is turning the idea of a missed opportunity into a blessing in disguise, or saying one door closed so another can open. These are wonderful ways to look at things, and the more you trust in yourself and your intuition and trust that everything will always work out in the end, the easier this type of thinking is. This is learning to trust the "holy flow" of life and will allow you to be happier and more at ease with life as it unfolds.

There is a consensus in the field of positive psychology that success does not fuel happiness. Actually, happiness fuels success. Shawn Achor, author of *The Happiness Advantage*, has spent over a decade researching this topic and has studied small ways to increase your happiness so you can retrain your brain to be more positive. Through arduous research in both psychology and neuroscience, his studies indicate that when you think more positively, your brain is more creative, energetic, motivated, engaged, and productive. A few of his many suggestions include journaling a positive event from the previous 24 hours (forcing you to focus on a positive experience), exercise (trains the brain to understand that behaviors matter), meditation (releasing stress, which gets in the way of positive thoughts), and random acts of kindness (for example, sending an email praising someone else first thing every day teaches you to give out kindness, which will send out attraction points for it to return to you).

These are all wonderful suggestions, and he has many more you can read about in his published studies and books. But I'd really like to focus on meditation and yoga, as both have proven to be extremely effective in my life, as well as in the lives of many others I know. Meditation releases stress that has been built up over our entire lives. We live in this culture of multitasking and constant communication. The demands are getting greater and greater, while the support is lessening and lessening. We are expected to do more with less and take on more roles than ever previously expected of a single human. Meditation teaches us to be healthier and more mindful while being less distracted. There are many types of meditation and some may resonate with you more than others. The goal for me is to reduce stress in a reliable, practical, and scientifically proven manner.

Meditation teaches us the ability to be mindful of what we are thinking. I had no idea how many thoughts were swirling around in my head all day every day until I learned the art of meditation. Not only did meditation open my eyes to the quantity of thoughts, but to the quality as well, which was in direct relation to my inner beliefs and deep programing. I started to notice patterns in my thoughts that were strongly correlated with my experiences in life. Once I started watching my thoughts during meditation, I was able to disassociate from them. Many thoughts were told to me as a child and have been playing like a broken record in my subconscious mind. Once I started to recognize recurring thoughts, I was able to see them as something other than me. That was a huge step as it allowed me to break loose of the hold those thoughts had on me. As soon as I noticed them and disassociated from them, I was able to slow them down or completely stop them. Then, I replaced them with a better belief.

Meditation impacts your health, happiness, cohesiveness, and cooperation. Daily meditation allows you the opportunity to step back, familiarize yourself with the present moment, and experience a greater sense of focus, clarity, and peacefulness. Meditation enables you to process the mental stimuli you are constantly bombarded with. This processing allows your brain to let the issue, problem, subject, or thought go so it doesn't continue to cause stress. Processing time is very important and, if meditation isn't right for you, there are other ways of achieving it. Possibly a good night's sleep, a walk in the park (maybe even barefoot), a cup of tea, time in nature, yoga, various types of exercise, music, or pet therapy would be more suitable for you?

We've already touched upon yoga and its benefits, but I would be remiss if I didn't mention again what a wonderful tool it is for stress reduction. Yoga links breath and movement, strengthening the mind-body-spirit connection. It is a perfect blend of meditation, stress reduction, proper breathing, movement of the body, and flexibility and strength training of the body and mind.

If you don't find time to let your brain process the stress it endures every day, you could easily become ill. Have you ever gotten sick when you were extremely busy? Have you ever wondered why you get sick at the worst times imaginable? Your brain and body both need downtime to process everything life throws at them daily, even more so in stressful or busy times. If you don't offer this to yourself, your body will make a point of slowing you down, usually through illness. The human body is intelligent beyond measure, and if you don't give yours what it needs, you can be sure it will find a way to take it.

Have you ever given thought to the people you allow in your life and how their energy is affecting you? Think about how you feel after spending time with a friend who is upbeat and bubbly and is constantly telling you all the great things going on in her life, as well as putting a positive spin on everything you tell her about your life. She is encouraging and fun and motivated and offers help in any way she can. Think about the difference between this person and another who is the exact opposite. She is draining. She is always complaining. Her job is hard. She hates her boss. Her kids misbehave. She can't find a decent man to save her life. She has money issues. She can come up with twenty reasons why anything you want to do won't work.

One of these friends lifts you up, and the other brings you down. It's very important to start taking note of how people affect your energy and how you feel after you've been with them. Allowing draining people to stay in your life out of obligation is a form of self-abuse. This is one of those situations in life where you have to put yourself first, and sometimes doing so means eliminating certain people from your life. It's important to always surround yourself with people who lift you up. You must protect yourself to keep your sanity intact. This is of utmost importance. If you do not do this, little by little, these negative people rub off on you and can literally rob you of your energy. This energy drain eventually leads to stress, fatigue, and dis-ease.

I know many of us, especially women, have problems caring for ourselves. Society has taught us to be "people-pleasers." If this concept of self-care feels difficult to you, I want you to remember the idea of the "child within." You have a little child inside of you that needs to be cared for. The child within is where your innocence is housed.

Think about children and how open they are to new friends, showing love, learning new things, and being vulnerable. All of these attributes are important to keep your entire life, but it is all too common to put walls up around these attributes as things in life happen to make you think you must self-protect. These walls can stop you from truly loving others, showing your feelings openly and honestly, or expressing vulnerability. Unfortunately, you may have let the wrong people into your life over the years and may now be suffering the consequences of being closed off emotionally to the world.

The child within you still knows how to be loving, vulnerable, and open. But your walls may be high because you still have people in your life who abuse those qualities. You never let that child come out for fear of being hurt—and rightfully so when you are in an unhealthy environment! However, putting up walls can also prevent you from experiencing loving, fulfilling relationships. If you take action to remove the people from your life who would abuse you emotionally, you can feel safe to release your inner child.

Stop and think about who you allow to be around your innocent, loving, vulnerable child. Would you ever let someone who said negative or unkind things near your toddler? Would you ever let someone who didn't show compassion, kindness, or love near your newborn? How do you feel when your 8-year-old child comes home from school and tells you about a classmate who was bullying her? Do your Mama-Bear or Papa-Bear protective instincts come out? This is exactly how I want you to look at the child within yourself. Your inner child needs the exact same amount of protection. Without this protection, he or she will harden and hide behind the walls you create. That is not good for you, your family, or the world as a whole.

There might be important people in your life that you don't necessarily want to cut out, but if you've realized they are sucking your energy or adding negativity to your life, it might be time to have a talk with them. Explain to them (in a loving way) that they have been negative, and it has been affecting you in an adverse way. Maybe explain that every time you leave their presence, you feel down, but you love them so much that you hope the two of you can work on a solution together. Ask them to keep the negativity away from you. Then hold strict boundaries around the request. If they start down their negative path around you (which they will at the beginning because habits are hard to break), you have the right to ask them to stop in a very kind, loving way. This shift in the dynamic of your relationship may cause some problems between the two of you at the beginning, but if the relationship is strong and you are truly coming from a place of love, honesty, and wanting to better not only your life, but the relationship, the other person will thank you in the long run for not only having solved your issue, but for helping them in a major way.

Chapter 7 Checklist

1. Open your mind to the idea that you have created everything in your life thus far.

2. Appreciate the correlation between your:

- Actions and life situations.
- Thought processes and life situations.
- Upbringing and current life situations.

3. Replace the idea of "fault" with "responsibility" when it comes to how you've attracted your current life situations.

4. Take responsibility for your current life situations and transform them with new ways of thinking and acting.

5. Focus on gratitude.

- Purchase and start using a gratitude journal.

6. Stop focusing on (talking and thinking about) the things that aren't going right in your life.

7. Practice positive psychology in your life.

- Look at missed opportunities as blessings in disguise.
- Believe that even the people who upset you the most are there to help you learn a lesson.
  - Consider the lesson.
  - The people who upset you the most will only leave your life or stop upsetting you when you learn the lesson. They will no longer have a reason to be in your life if the lesson is learned.
- Believe that every challenge already has an answer.
  - Have fun finding the answer.
- Add daily movement to stimulate the happy hormones in your body.
- Meditate to reduce stress.
- Commit to one random act of kindness a day.

8. Let your brain process all the stimuli coming at it on a daily basis:

- Good sleep
- Walk in the park
- Cup of tea or alone time with no distractions
- Time in nature
- Time with family/children
- Yoga or other forms of body movement
- Music therapy
- Pet therapy

9. Decrease the amount of time spent with negative people.

10. Increase the amount of time spent with positive people.

11. Have a loving, open discussion with close people in your life who might be bringing you down.

- Offer to help them be more positive, thus improving your relationship and their life.

12. Be open to seeing walls that you have put up to protect yourself in the past.

- Identify why you still have those walls up.
- Identify what you need to do to bring them down.

13. Protect your inner child as you would protect your own child, not letting negativity into your life.

Chapter 8:

Practice Makes Perfect—Putting It All Together

Starting the journey to a mind-body-spirit connection will open doors in all avenues of your life. However, at times, it may feel confusing or overwhelming, so go slow and be deliberate in your approach. Our society and healthcare in the West do not traditionally emphasize the connection of mind, body, and spirit. This is why I have ended each chapter with upgrades that will help you switch to a more holistic lifestyle. If you choose a couple of options from each chapter that seem easy to incorporate into your life (as hopefully you've been doing while reading this book), you will slowly turn your lifestyle into a more holistic version of where you are today. And, as time goes on and those few upgrades become habit, you can choose a couple more to focus on. Again, as those become habit, chose a few more.

You will find as you make these changes that you will feel better, you will look better, you will start attracting better experiences into your life, and your quality of life will improve beyond your imagination. Once the momentum starts to build and you are feeling so wonderful, you will find that ways to improve your life even further will start to show up on your journey. New teachers, authors, experts, and ideas will reveal themselves as you are ready, and your life will take on a whole new direction towards holistic health and abundance.

I am not suggesting you finish reading this book and take yourself off all your medications. I am not suggesting you blindly search the internet for ways to holistically cure your disease. That would be irresponsible and irrational. The goal is to start making lifestyle modifications so the medication is no longer necessary. The goal is to take things slowly, see what works, and as you start feeling better, talk to your physician about what you've been doing. Then you can experiment with cutting your dosage down or coming off your medication completely. If you've had high cholesterol your whole life and are on a cholesterol-lowering medication, eating a plant-based diet for a few weeks and taking yourself off your medication is not a good plan of action. However, moving to a plant-based diet for a few months, then talking to your physician about the changes you've made and asking to cut your dosage while being monitored closely might be a move your physician is willing to take.

Maybe your physician will ask you to get weekly cholesterol tests as soon as the modification is made to your medication, and if those numbers are good for a few months, you can drop the dosage again. Having your physician there to monitor your progress and help you understand your numbers is key to making these types of changes. If you find your physician is unwilling and you feel strongly about your ability to make lifestyle changes that can help you reduce your medications, maybe it's time to find a physician who is more in line with your thought process.

Dr. Joel Kahn, author of *The Whole Heart Solution: Halt Heart Disease Now with the Best of Alternative and Traditional Medicine*, is not only one of my favorite authors and physicians, but a perfect example of the type of physician who understands both ends of the spectrum. Traditionally trained and one of the brightest people I have ever met, he started to see the correlation between lifestyle and disease as he worked in his practice. He saw what the medical community refused to look at or teach, and he dove headfirst into that world to find out for himself what it was all about. He's since become an expert on the subject, writing books, articles, and papers while traveling the globe as a speaker and leader in the field of holistic heart therapy. If you want to learn more about heart disease and holistic ways of healing it, this book is a must read.

Unfortunately, not all physicians out there are like Dr. Kahn, and they feel the subject of holistic medicine is nonsense. And I understand why they would think that. It's not that they are bad people or bad physicians; it's that the majority of the medical training they've received does not cover the subject of lifestyle, behavior, or holistic ways to treat disease. Many medical schools are funded by big pharma or other medical institutions that believe in the Westernized approach to medicine. There are big industries and institutions with big money that have a vested interest in things staying the way they are in Westernized medicine. In my opinion, none of these industries or institutions is wrong or bad. As a matter of fact, they were started with very noble intentions to use new technology to save the world, and in many instances, they have.

Think about all the wonderful advancements in medicine— the newborn babies it has saved, the ability to put a body back together after a tragic accident, the widespread diseases that have been controlled or eradicated, the life support given to bodies that needed a chance to build strength back up and heal in order to live. I personally have a fantastic story of recovery with Westernized medicine's help after shattering my tibia in a martial arts (self-defense) class. If it weren't for modern medicine, I might have never walked again, but luckily, they were able to use a cadaver bone to rebuild my tibia. After a year of intense healing and therapy, I walked unassisted again, albeit with a severe limp. Then slowly, as I practiced yoga, strengthened my muscles, and improved my flexibility, the limp subsided, and now, a decade later, it's like it never happened.

The unfortunate parts of disease management in Western medicine are the long-term effects of medication and the unnatural ingredients inside of them. This is where I feel modern medicine missed the mark. Rather than looking at the cause of increased disease in the United States, they looked to mask the problem with a pill. Not only is it far more lucrative to create a pill for every ailment, but it plays into people's desire for a quick fix. And with that quick-fix mentality, most consumers would prefer to take a pill than change their lifestyle. They have deep-rooted habits, beliefs, and self-defeating thoughts that make them undermine their own success. Couple that with addictions to food and unhealthy lifestyles, physicians who haven't studied alternative therapies, and a society that pushes the growth of big-profit industries, and it becomes very difficult for the common consumer to make holistic changes. This is not a small problem, but it is a problem that can be solved.

One by one, we can solve this problem. As each of us individually wakes up to our own reality and starts making the changes necessary, the way we spend our dollars will drive the change in the world. When we stop buying processed foods, the food industry will be forced to follow the demand for whole, unprocessed foods. When we only purchase organic produce, the produce industry will harvest more organic produce. When we stop buying skincare and household cleaning products that contain harmful chemicals, the industry leaders will start to produce more products without chemicals. When we choose to support companies and corporations that are doing the right thing despite their increased cost, we are giving energy and support to the change we want to see. When we purchase books about holistic living, we support those authors so they can create more books supporting our cause and helping us live better.

Our money supports what we purchase, so maybe it's time we look at the expensive option a bit differently. Maybe it's time to pay that extra money for the things we believe in. When we all do this, we will change the world, but it starts with each one of us making the change for ourselves so we can collectively make a global impact.

Please remember the most important thing to focus on when making changes towards a healthier life (and life is general) is to be at ease with the process. Life is meant to be lived. Life is meant to be fun, spontaneous, exciting, and full of love and all things good. Stressing out about being healthy is not part of that equation. Finding your way to health, wellness, and happiness is a process best walked with ease and a light heart. Incorporate what you can with as much ease as possible. Start attracting easy health upgrades into your life. Start attracting people in your life who make you laugh and help create your new world of health in a fun way. Be open to new possibilities and incorporate new ways to improve your health when they feel right to you. Don't force anything. Don't force yourself to eat foods you hate. Find foods you love that are healthy and eat more of those. Find food substitutions for your favorite foods that are less processed or have fewer additives, then swap out what you are currently eating for these healthier choices.

Your taste buds will change. They acclimate and actually start to crave whatever types of food you eat. This is the key to modifying your behavior around food. Change would never happen if you had to deprive yourself for the rest of your life. But if you truly start enjoying the healthy foods, it's extremely easy to eat healthy foods. It just becomes your preference.

Maybe you've heard that meat isn't the best for you, but it's so incorporated into your diet that you're not sure how to go about lessening your intake. What if you just replaced red meat with white meat occasionally? Then, over time, maybe replace white meat with fish occasionally. This is how I started my path to vegetarianism. It was slow, it took me a few years, but I never even noticed the difference. Over time, I didn't want meat. I got so in tune with my body that meat no longer appealed to me. It made me feel too full, heavy, and just gross. Then it just stopped tasting good to me. There is a big difference between depriving oneself of something and just eventually not wanting it anymore.

When I was diagnosed with Crohn's dis-ease and wanted to change my life, the first thing I intuitively did was introduce a lot of raw vegetables into my diet. I made Sunday my day for grocery shopping and went out and purchased a large amount of raw vegetables. As soon as I got home, I immediately washed and chopped all the vegetables so I could put them in little baggies for easy "grab and go" food. I found that when I made healthy foods accessible, I actually ate them, which was a new practice for me. And, as it turns out, this is a very effective practice.

What could life changes as simple as this do for you? Could you find yourself eating less processed food? Maybe you'll stop visiting the vending machine at work or going out to fast food restaurants because you will have food on hand that is healthy and easy. Various dips (hummus is a great choice) and salsas can make the veggies more pleasing. What about swapping your table salt out for Celtic or Himalayan sea salt? Can you switch from a very processed and additive filled veggie dip to a natural, no additive hummus? How about an all-natural, GMO free, organic salsa with organic chips made from brown rice, flax, or sesame seeds and quinoa? They're out there, I assure you. It takes just a bit of time to read packages in your local health food store to find a few good options. As soon as you find a couple of new brands you like, you'll have a whole new diet full of natural and healthy foods that taste just as good (if not better) than the ones you used to eat.

As a side note and reminder, you'll want to read ingredients versus trusting labels on packages. Unfortunately, the food industry and manufacturers spend a great deal of money on marketing and know that many of us are looking for healthy upgrades. They're very clever and will put things on their packaging such as "natural" or "organic" while they still have chemicals, additives, and other harmful substances in the food. If you look at the ingredients list, you will notice what is truly inside of the product. As a rule of thumb, if you know all the words in the ingredients list and they truly are foods that grow out of the earth, you are good to go!

This example is about food, but you can see how slowly incorporating healthy upgrades into your life can start to change your life. It's all about baby steps, and if you can slowly start advancing your health over time, you will be a new person a year from now. Your tissues, bones, and organs regenerate. Food is used to create new cells, which means you are literally becoming what you eat. Your body uses food, as well as your beliefs and thoughts, to reshape the new cells that are forming in your body. This is very powerful knowledge that will help you to understand how easy it is to recreate your body and achieve true health. I don't care where you are today. I don't care how sick, tired, old, or unhealthy you are. It is absolutely possible to achieve health at any stage of life.

One of the greatest gifts you can give yourself is the gift of trusting yourself. Learn how to communicate with your higher self. Learn to sit in meditation, even if only for three or four minutes and listen for the answers. Practice asking yourself what is best for you in any given moment. When faced with a decision that I am unsure of, I will often sit down in a quiet room, even if only for two minutes, take a few deep, cleansing breaths to settle my mind and body, then ask myself, "What is the best decision I could make for all involved?" At first, the answers didn't always come easily or clearly. But after a few weeks of doing this and with some trial and error, I was able to clearly hear the answers.

Every answer is inside of you. You just have muddied the waters and are having a difficult time seeing it. If you learn how to listen and then start to trust your intuition, you can never go wrong. This can be from something as insignificant as, "Will this vitamin help me?" to something of life-changing significance, such as, "Will this treatment cure my cancer?" Flexing this muscle and learning to listen to your own intuition is a powerful practice that will change your life.

Now you realize that you have a language by which the body communicates with you and that spirit sends you signals and messages through illnesses, injuries, dis-ease, or any other feelings in your body. Likewise, the body also sends signals of being on the right track, such as joy, love, fulfillment, energy, vitality, health, and happiness. Learning to tune in and listen to your body, follow its signs, and heed its warnings is crucial on the path to wellness. All the tools necessary to take your life to the next level of vitality, health, and happiness are now in your hands. I commend you on your open-mindedness and you willingness and desire to walk down this road. You will be rewarded in more ways than you can imagine for walking this path, and I am honored to be on your journey with you. Thank you!

Chapter 8 Checklist

1. Review previous chapters for additional upgrades available to you.

2. Research or purchase literature on the subjects or various authors mentioned that intrigued you.

3. Identify which leg of the mind-body-spirit tripod you feel to be most weak in your life.

- Consider a plan to focus on that specific leg (mind, body, or spirit).

4. If your current physician or medical practitioner does not respect your desire to integrate modern and holistic/alternative medicine, consider finding one that does.

5. Can you support companies, brands, and people who are teaching, selling, and advancing the fields you believe are important to not only your personal health and happiness, but that of society and the planet?

6. Can you find a way to incorporate this new information and these new upgrades in a gentle and loving manner?

7. Can you avoid being preachy to those around you once you start reaping the benefits of your newfound holistic lifestyle and allow them to see the change in you and come to you for help when/if they are ready?

8. Can you slowly start to swap out healthier versions of your favorite foods for the current versions?

9. Can you start to read ingredient lists on packaged foods, looking for chemicals as closely as some count calories?

10. Can you start to trust yourself and your intuition to guide you to what serves your body, mind, and spirit best?

11. Can you start to meditate daily, if for only three minutes each morning?

- Download a guided meditation app
- Count to ten over and over in your head
- Count your inhales and exhales
- Repeat a mantra or a word over and over in your head
- Hold a mala (prayer beads) and move from bead to bead, repeating a mantra or prayer on each

12. Can you learn to see your dis-ease or injury as a blessing in disguise?

13. Can you learn to accept that spirit communicates with you through your body if you are not hearing the subtle signs in your daily life?

14. Can you learn to see the subtle signs as communication before dis-ease manifests in your body?

Chapter 9

Conclusion

If life is a journey full of twists and turns, you now have a roadmap in your possession to guide you in transforming your health through a greater mind-body-spirit connection. You no longer have to feel lost or hopeless or believe that the problems, mistakes, and missteps in your life have been in vain. As I have taken you through my personal story of health and life transformation, I hope you can see how all aspects of my past—the good, the bad, and the ugly—have played an essential role in creating the person I am today. And the same is true for you.

You should now be able to look back at your own life and see your experiences as working together to bring you to this very moment. You are here now, present, mindful, and aware that you no longer have to travel through life just going through the motions, feeling sick and sad, doing what everyone expects of you and what everyone tells you to do. You have options. You have tools. You are strong and becoming stronger every day as you strive to establish new healthy, life-changing habits. Life is an adventure and you are living in the best days, starting now, because your mind, body, and spirit are awakening to all that life can be.

Whether you have faced chronic pain, dis-ease or debilitating depression, shame over your appearance, deep emotional scars from abuse, or a lack of inspiration and direction—it really doesn't matter what the struggles have been in your life because your mind is being transformed to see it all in a different way. You can use these life experiences to make different choices, to rise above your past, and to be all that you dream you can be. You can begin each day focusing on gratitude in order to attract more goodness in your life. You have been enlightened and the path ahead of you is well lit.

Of course, this doesn't mean every step along the way will be easy or problem-free. On the contrary, you will likely experience resistance from others and even from within. You may find family members or friends do not like you trying to change your life because it makes them uncomfortable or it makes them feel poorly about themselves. Please understand—this is not your problem.

You may discover along the way that these people who do not support your journey will pull away for a time, only to come back and want to learn from you when they see the positive changes manifest in your life. Or…you may find they stay away. Either way, it is okay. You are growing healthier, stronger, and wiser and you can handle whatever relationship issues may come your way. Because you understand that it is absolutely vital for you to protect your inner child, you have no room for people in your life who are less than supportive or unwilling to accept the person you are becoming.

When it comes to the resistance from within, you can be prepared to face it head-on. Old habits die hard, and there may be some growing pains as you let go of unhealthy habits and bring new healthy habits into your life. You can think of this pain as birthing pains—you are birthing the new you. This new you will be a person who is true to herself, who allows herself to enjoy the fullness of emotions and human experiences life has to offer. As this new person, you will make choices—lifestyle, nutritional, relational, spiritual—that will encourage continual growth and fine-tuning, enabling you to feel your best in all areas of your life.

But you will do all of this with great ease and peace. Remember, this isn't about striving for perfection. This is a journey, and there will be bumps in the road. You can count on it. So it is important to always give yourself grace for the slip-ups. I don't call them setbacks, because when you are aware and connected, you realize these aren't setbacks but rather learning experiences and opportunities to grow stronger and wiser. If you begin to feel frustrated with yourself, remember that precious inner child and how you should talk to a child—encouraging, loving, and kind—never with a spirit of condemnation, disgust, or anger.

It is also important to go slow and enjoy each step of the journey, learning as much from each new phase as you can. Because you will be going slowly, you will also be able to stay mindful of what is happening around you and what is unfolding before you. You will be ready when spirit brings people, ideas, and experiences to you. When you are in tune with yourself, it will be easy to see which choices are right for you and which ones support your journey to a connected mind-body-spirit.

In addition to this book resource I've shared with you, I've provided you with names of several other professionals who can guide you in this journey through their books and information. As you move forward, it will be important to continually seek wisdom from others who have extensive experience in creating and growing that mind-body-spirit connection. Yes, it's likely you will be a life-long learner because once you get a taste of how exciting and life-giving knowledge can be, you will hunger for more. The good news is there is always more to learn and experience, so this journey will never be dull and it will never end as long as you live.

As I wrap up this book, it keeps coming to my mind to remind you that all of this will take practice. It may take a while for you to get the hang of incorporating more green vegetables into your diet, or cutting out processed foods completely. It may take a while for you to learn to shut out the negative voices in your mind and replace them with a positive voice. It may take a while for you to wipe off the windshield to your soul so you can get in touch with spirit. In fact, you may have to wipe the mud off the windshield to your soul every single day for a while until you reach a higher level of connectedness. It's OKAY. There is no pressure in this very intimate journey. You have your whole life ahead of you to dive deeper and deeper into your beautiful mind-body-spirit connection. That's exactly why I call it a journey and not a task. A task has a deadline, but your journey does not.

I'm so honored to have been a part of your journey and envision amazing things ahead for you in the days, months, and years to come. From this day forward, may you walk in good health and with ease and wonder, taking in all life has to offer you as you grow, flourish, and life live to the fullest.

Connect with Me

Visit my website to continue with me on a journey to mind, body, and spirit wellbeing. Go to <u>CassieSobelton.com</u>, to sign up for my e-newsletter, connect with me on social media, read my personal blog, and watch videos filled with simple tips to upgrade your health. All of this at no cost to you!

One Last Thing...

Thank you for joining me on my continuing journey to mind, body, and spirit wellness! I hope my experiences will help to guide you on a path that empowers you to get back to balance. If you've found my story helpful, I would ask, in gratitude, for a just a moment of your time to give this book a quick review on Amazon.

Thanks again!

Cassie

About the Author

Cassie's journey to wellness started in her early 20s. As a hardworking corporate professional, Cassie was working over 60 hours a week, often burning the midnight oil. Investing more time in work meant less time dedicated to taking care of herself, which ultimately lead to her failing health, dozens of surgeries and medications, and a diagnosis of Crohn's disease, a chronic inflammatory condition of the gastrointestinal tract. Out of the pain and frustration of that experience, Cassie found clarity by turning to mind, body, and spirit balance.

Cassie began to make dramatic changes in her life. She changed her diet, began focusing on her spiritual well-being, and started exercising on a regular basis. Within a year, she had lost 40 pounds and alleviated her need for medication. As a living testament to making wellness a priority, Cassie began counseling hundreds of people a year who also wanted to take charge of their health and, ultimately, their lives.

Realizing she wasn't the only one allowing a corporate commitment to take a toll on her health, and that others were looking also for guidance, she started SynBella, a corporate employee wellness company that teaches people to THRIVE in the workplace.